The Genius of James Thurber

THE GENIUS OF

JAMES THURBER

Selection and introduction
by Michael J. Rosen

THE FOLIO SOCIETY
London 1997

Set in Berkeley at The Folio Society
Printed on Ibis Wove and bound at
The Bath Press, Avon using a blocked
design by Helen Smithson.

CONTENTS

INTRODUCTION

In 1953, less than a month before its commencement exercises, one P. Leslie Woodbine, president of Eureka College in Eureka, Illinois, mailed James Thurber a letter offering him 'the honourary degree of Doctor of Letters'. Thurber received and accepted several such degrees during his life, although that very weekend he was, regretfully, to be at yet another college accepting the very same honour. Two weeks later, a letter from Burrus Dickinson, the president of Eureka College, answered Thurber's reply, reporting that 'the Woodbine letter was a hoax and I am sorry if any inconvenience to you was involved. Perhaps, indeed, the recognition by a student might mean as much to you as the degree if it had been authorized by the college.' To this all too casual palliative (why Mr Dickinson hadn't chosen to save face and honour his own little college by authorising such a degree, no doubt escapes the reader as it does me), Thurber wrote an uncharacteristically mild reply. (Recall that he once described himself to *Life* magazine thus: 'I am in a corner without being backed there and often come out fighting.')

I don't really know the etiquette that should be followed in such a predicament as mine, but I feel that I owe you and Eureka College my sincere apologies. In my college days we played pranks too, but not on aging blind humorists. We selected stuffed shirts. If I had been able to read the letter head I received and to examine the typing and the signature, I don't think I would have been taken in. I was on the point of having my secretary reply signing her name Virginia Creeper, but I do not regard honor or honors as a fitting subject for kidding around. As for the name of the mythical president, it is surely not an unlikely one for the Middle West. An authentic honor was recently extended to me in a letter from an Ohio woman authentically named Mrs Depew Head. I am a friend of a distinguished Ohioan named H. Morton Bodfish, and I'm a mild authority on a celebrated Bermudian gentleman named H. Outerbridge Horsey. As for

7

my falling for a degree offered on such short notice, I can only report that I was offered one on the identical short notice by a Middle Western State university three years ago. Incidentally, I turned that one down. I am certainly glad that I did not reject the mythical one.

I am afraid I do not regard this hoax as a sign of 'appreciation' by a student. If writers my age depended on appreciation from the modern college student, we would probably languish of some kind of malnutrition. I have several times pointed out in recent years that humor is dying in America, a terrifying thing, but not a surprising one in view of the condition of the world, the plight of our species, and the fearful state of the American mind and spirit. I hate to see humor replaced by vulgarity and cruelty, but I'm afraid that's what we're in for.

We are now nearly fifty years from Thurber's prediction about the state of humour. Opinions are probably mixed about the degree to which 'vulgarity and cruelty' have become a part of contemporary humour, but one thing is clear: to judge from the proliferation of recent biographies of Thurber and new editions of his work, attention to and recognition of Thurber is anything but languishing. We are, as well, just past a hundred years since James Thurber's birth in 1894. How perfect (and yes, how daunting, at least to me) to prepare a single testament to James Thurber's genius.

As a fitting re-introduction to the humorist, here is a self-portrait concocted from excerpts of autobiographical send-offs penned at various points in his career. I have supplied a few factual landmarks amid this career which spans eighteen collections of writings and drawings, two books of fables, two memoirs, two perennially performed Broadway hits, and five children's books.

To begin: 'James Thurber was born in Columbus, Ohio, where so many awful things happened to him, on December 8, 1894. He was unable to keep anything on his stomach until he was seven years old but grew to be 6 feet $1\frac{1}{4}$ inches tall and to weigh a hundred fifty-four fully dressed for winter.' He was 'born in the blowy uplands of Columbus, Ohio, in a district known as "the Flats", which, for half of the year, was partially underwater and during the rest of the time was an outcropping of live granite, rising in dry weather to a height of two hundred feet. This condition led to moroseness, skepticism, jumping when shots were fired, membership in a silver cornet band, and, finally, a system of floating pulley-baskets by means of which the Thurber family was raised up to and lowered down from the second floor of the old family homestead.'

In truth, Thurber's childhood did include two life-long influences: his mother's uncanny and often mischievous sense of dramatic humour, and the injury to his sight sustained during a game of William Tell in which Thurber took an arrow in the eye. ('Sympathetic ophthalmia' eventually overtook the other eye, leaving him blind amid a burgeoning career.) Owing to this, his school days began with a certain frailty and introspection, though his years at East High School blossomed with honours, the class presidency, and initial recognition of his writing and drawing abilities.

Thurber's studies at The Ohio State University included some predicaments, such as botany; instead of seeing 'a vivid, restless clockwork of sharply defined plant cells', Thurber saw 'what looks like a lot of milk'. Another low-point was military drill. 'At eleven o'clock each morning thousands of freshmen and sophomores used to deploy over the campus, moodily creeping up on the old chemistry building . . . As a soldier I was never any good at all . . . Once General Littlefield, who was commandant of the cadet corps, popped up in front of me during regimental drill and snapped, "You are the main trouble with this university!" I think he meant that my type was the main trouble with the university but he may have meant me individually.'

Thurber did drop out temporarily during his sophomore year for his own programme of reading and movie-going. But he had met Elliott Nugent, with whom he would subsequently write *The Male Animal*, whose own theatrical gifts and energy redirected some of Thurber's unchannelled creativity. Thurber then began to write for the school newspaper, as well as edit the *Sundial*, OSU's humour magazine, and played active roles in The Strollers dramatic club, writing plays and songs. Without a degree, he left the university 'in June, 1918, but I couldn't get into the army on account of my sight, just as grandfather

9

couldn't get in on account of his age. He applied several times and each time he took off his coat and threatened to whip the men who said he was too old.'

In *My Life and Hard Times*, which remained on the best-seller list for most of 1945, Thurber recounted the most memorable moments of his college days spent in the Victorian structure the Thurbers rented from 1913 to 1918, which is now the Thurber House, an historic landmark, museum and cultural centre. This is the legendary house where the ghost got in, alarms were heard in the night, the bed fell on father, and electricity leaked from the empty sockets when the wall switches weren't turned off. (The five larger-than-life, limestone Thurber dogs now digging and sniffing in the Reading Garden are not part of the original landmark – we added them, along with a bronze unicorn munching lilies in the garden, in the years since the house opened in 1984.)

'The mistaken exits and entrances of my thirties have moved me several times to some thought of spending the rest of my days wandering aimlessly around the South Seas, like a character out of Conrad, silent and inscrutable. But the necessity for frequent visits to my oculist and dentist has prevented this . . . Nobody from Columbus has ever made a first rate wanderer in the Conradean tradition. Some of them have been fairly good at disappearing for a few days to turn up in a hotel in Louisville with a bad headache and no recollection of how they got there . . .' Though Thurber lived in New York, Connecticut, Bermuda, and France, Columbus remained a well-spring for much of his best work. 'Columbus is a town in which almost anything is likely to happen and in which almost everything has.'

In 1927, after writing his 'Credos and Curios' columns for *The Columbus Dispatch* (an admixture of brief reviews, parodies, editorials, and commentary that presages his future work), a stint at the Paris edition of *The Tribune*, and frustrating attempts at selling humorous pieces, and settling into his first marriage to Althea Adams, with whom he conceived one daughter, he met E. B. White, who arranged a meeting with Harold Ross, the editor of a then-struggling new magazine, *The New Yorker*. Thurber was hired as managing editor and, so he claimed, worked his way down to writer. In collaboration with

White, he published *Is Sex Necessary?*, a parody of the popular sex/psychology books of the day. They wrote alternate chapters and Thurber provided quick pencil sketches that White inked. 'It was, to be sure, E. B. White . . . who first began to look at my drawings critically. Like the discovery of San Salvador and the discovery of pommes soufflé, the discovery of my art was an accident.' With White's encouragement, Thurber began to submit artwork to *The New Yorker*, where he would publish hundreds of cartoons and spot illustrations before blindness overtook him. Dorothy Parker once wrote, 'These are strange people that Mr Thurber has turned loose upon us. They seem to fall into three classes – the playful, the defeated, and the ferocious. All of them have the outer semblance of unbaked cookies . . . It is curious, perhaps terrible, how Mr Thurber has influenced the American face and physique, and some day he will surely answer for it. People didn't go about looking like that before he started drawing.' Nor did cartoons themselves 'go about looking like that' until Thurber arrived on the scene.

Married now to his second wife Helen Wismer, and ensconced in Connecticut for the most part, Thurber worked steadily, creating an enormously varied and rich canon of writing and drawings. Between 1930 and 1961 he published nearly thirty books. Many of them collected the unparalleled range of pieces written for *The New Yorker* and other magazines: the 'casuals' featured in 'Talk of the Town'; profiles of tennis stars and nearly forgotten public figures; parodies of literary figures of the day, pulp magazines, and current events; and scores of stories such as 'The Catbird Seat' and 'The Secret Life of Walter Mitty', two of the most anthologised pieces of modern fiction.

In his heyday, Thurber's cartoons appeared in galleries (Henri Matisse once said that 'a man named Thurber . . . is the only good artist you have in New York'); his illustrations powered advertising campaigns for Fisher Body, Bug-a-Boo insecticide, and The French Line cruise ships; companies such as Bergdorf Goodman manufactured Thurber-inspired clothing and tableware; and admirers and reviewers world wide sang Thurber's praises. On the arrival of *Men, Women and Dogs*, W. Somerset Maugham wrote, 'It's the perfect book to turn over while one is drinking a cocktail. The only thing against it is that it makes a cocktail seem rather wan & pale.'

At large, and getting larger, Thurber contributed articles widely on subjects that ranged from the international spy situation to the future of photography, from the development of the bicycle to Byrd's discoveries in Antarctica. Though he hardly possessed genuine familiarity with these topics, he addressed each with the borrowed tone and speech of an expert; and therein lay a style of humour that has outlasted generations of imitators.

'Quick to arouse, he is very hard to quiet and people often just go away,' Thurber once described himself in print, and, perhaps, in jest. 'He never listens when anybody else is talking, preferring to keep his mind a blank until they get through so he can talk.' Though his last years were especially troubled with the burdens of his physical and mental condition, Thurber continued to be a vivacious raconteur, a passionate debater, and, as the occasion provided, an exasperating guest. As his friend the novelist Peter DeVries wrote, 'If in his art he told the truth, in his life he told it off.' Shortly before his death, Thurber did manage to write a Broadway hit, *The Thurber Carnival*, a theatrical revue of his work directed by Burgess Meredith; for several weeks, he even took the stage and acted.

Despite the rounds of operations and treatments for eye problems, a near-death encounter with pneumonia, a toxic thyroid condition, a series of strokes, arteriosclerosis, and the accompanying psychological strain from these and from the alcohol in which he sought release, Thurber continued to create, becoming, so he claimed, 'an ear writer', prevailing upon his formidable memory which could retain two thousand words of prose for a later dictation session.

'Thurber's life baffles and irritates the biographer because of its lack of design,' he pretended to write as his own biographer. 'One has the disturbing feeling that the man contrived to be some place without actually having gone there.' And yet, wherever it is he finally did manage to go, readers everywhere have been only too glad to follow.

Which brings us again to the present volume. Although I have lived (and I don't mean merely figuratively) among Thurber's stories and drawings for fifteen years, and although I have ransacked, or at least read, as much of his uncollected and even unpublished material as the estate has made available, I have not, until this occasion, had to choose among the work those items that would compose a consummate volume. In two previous volumes of Thurber's uncollected though for the most part published work – prose and drawings that appeared in newspapers or magazines – I attempted to restore a neglected part of his canon. Neglected, I have suggested, because his own blindness, as well as his own driven, ongoing projects, propelled him into new endeavours rather than toward any comprehensive review of previous material. Moreover, the piquancy or potency of some pieces may have seemed diminished to the author at, say, a distance of two or three decades. He once said in an interview, 'I guess books of humour don't last because, like the passions, humour is a changing thing. It is likely to date because it deals in the modern idiom.' But we are at a more generous distance now, some forty-five years since his death in 1961. What has become clear is this: so much of James Thurber's work is, like fine wine, extraordinary both for its original creation and for its present drinkability, allowing us to appreciate both the times in which he wrote and our own time.

Allowing that many favourites have been passed over in my culling, permit me to set forth a few of my criteria. Ultimately, this anthology reflects my tastes, my sense of humour, and my understanding of his canon. And so I grant the reader that these inclusions may reflect nothing more noble than prejudice, nothing more scholarly than predilection.

For the sake of variety as well as coherence, I have not excerpted his two volumes of fables, preferring to keep them an intact whole: not a mere selection of witty morals, but a cagey indictment of American culture as it revved its wheels before World War II, and spun its wheels after, unhinged by McCarthy's campaigns. Likewise, I have left for supplementary reading the whole of his two plainly autobiographical excursions into biography: *The Years with Ross*, his memoir of *The New Yorker* and its editor, and *The Thurber Album*, appreciations of family and key influences in his earlier Columbus years. Moreover, I did not allocate pages for Thurber's lively tributes to other writers or public figures, feeling that in this limited context Thurber should be trained almost exclusively on himself.

At the other end of the spectrum, I preferred to overlook many interesting pieces that reveal Thurber at his most artfully indulgent or introspective: both those longer works centred on word play or vocabulary, and his more agitated diatribes. I declined exemplary pieces that were not utterly forthcoming but required some editorial intervention or explanation in favour of those in which any small allusions to no-longer-current figures or events could either be glossed over or their meaning gleaned from the context.

Confined to their original volumes are, as well, several well-known works whose deprecations (regarding women, race, or certain nationalities) might overwhelm such a work at this later – can we boast, more 'advanced' – state in time? Even though humour must, by its very commission, occupy those territories where we are most uncomfortable, most fidgety with the reassessments of politics, order and privilege, at this oh-so-proud distance of half a century such jocular attention to those somewhat assuaged topics may strike a present reader as unduly juvenile or pitiable. And yet, what benighted attitudes and bigotries will another half-century claim of our present-day humour?

I wanted each included cartoon to say, as the one on page 188 literally does, 'Touché!', striking the reader with its sword of apt absurdity. (Thurber's sword decapitates, yes, but bloodlessly, harmlessly, theoretically even, suggesting that humour both cuts to the quick and invites us, via our laughter's admission, into the relative safety of its spectacle.)

Finally, I was and am still willing to admit that my selections fall short. Thurber greatly exceeds this book, but not his shelf of books in the library. And so, rather than be resigned to this, I feel somewhat like Thurber's clairvoyant on page 160 who replies to her young client: 'I can't get in touch with your uncle, but there's a horse here that wants to say hallo.' So here is, if not the genius of James Thurber, at least a genial thoroughbred with which to spend the hours. It is, as well, a seriously tendered honour, one that I hope the great man would accept.

MICHAEL J. ROSEN

THE PET DEPARTMENT

The idea for the department was suggested by the daily pet column in the New York Evening Post, *and by several others.*

Q. I enclose a sketch of the way my dog, William, has been lying for two days now. I think there must be something wrong with him. Can you tell me how to get him out of this?

MRS L. L. G.

A. I should judge from the drawing that William is in a trance. Trance states, however, are rare with dogs. It may just be ecstasy. If at the end of another twenty-four hours he doesn't seem to be getting anywhere, I should give him up. The position of the ears leads me to believe that he may be enjoying himself in a quiet way, but the tail is somewhat alarming.

Q. Our cat, who is thirty-five, spends all of her time in bed. She follows every move I make, and this is beginning to get to me. She never seems sleepy nor particularly happy. Is there anything I could give her?

MISS L. Mc.

A. There are no medicines which can safely be given to induce felicity in a cat, but you might try lettuce, which is a soporific, for the wakefulness. I would have to see the cat watching you to tell whether anything could be done to divert her attention.

Q. My husband, who is an amateur hypnotiser, keeps trying to get our bloodhound under his control. I contend that this is not doing the dog any good. So far he has not yielded to my husband's influence, but I am afraid that if he once got under, we couldn't get him out of it.

A. A. T.

A. Dogs are usually left cold by all phases of psychology, mental telepathy, and the like. Attempts to hypnotise this particular breed, however, are likely to be fraught with a definite menace. A bloodhound, if stared at fixedly, is liable to gain the impression that it is under suspicion, being followed, and so on. This upsets a bloodhound's life, by completely reversing its whole scheme of behaviour.

Q. My wife found this owl in the attic among a lot of ormolu clocks and old crystal chandeliers. We can't tell whether it's stuffed or only dead. It is sitting on a strange and almost indescribable sort of iron dingbat.

MR MOLLEFF

A. What your wife found is a museum piece – a stuffed cockatoo. It looks to me like a rather botchy example of taxidermy. This is the first stuffed bird I have ever seen with its eyes shut, but whoever had it stuffed probably wanted it stuffed that way. I couldn't say what the thing it is sitting on is supposed to represent. It looks broken.

Q. Our gull cannot get his head down any further than this, and bumps into things.

H. L. F.

A. You have no ordinary gull to begin with. He looks to me a great deal like a rabbit backing up. If he *is* a gull, it is impossible to keep him in the house. Naturally he will bump into things. Give him his freedom.

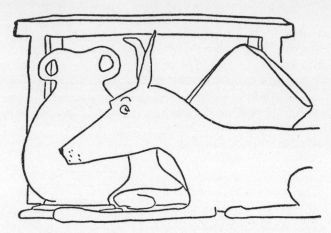

Q. My police dog has taken to acting very strange, on account of my father coming home from work every night for the past two years and saying to him, 'If you're a police dog, where's your badge?' after which he laughs (my father).

ELLA R.

A. The constant reiteration of any piece of badinage some-times has the same effect on present-day neurotic dogs that it has on people. It is dangerous and thoughtless to twit a police dog on his powers, authority, and the like. From the way your dog seems to hide behind tables, large vases, and whatever that thing is that looks like a suitcase, I should imagine that your father has carried this thing far enough – perhaps even too far.

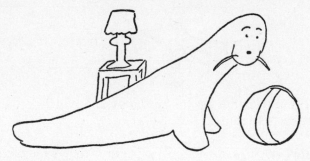

Q. My husband's seal will not juggle, although we have tried everything.

GRACE H.

A.   Most seals will not juggle; I think I have never known one that juggled. Seals balance things, and sometimes toss objects (such as the large ball in your sketch) from one to another. This last will be difficult if your husband has but one seal. I'd try him in plain balancing, beginning with a billiard cue or something. It may be, of course, that he is a non-balancing seal.

Q.   We have a fish with ears and wonder if it is valuable.

JOE WRIGHT

A.   I find no trace in the standard fish books of any fish with ears. Very likely the ears do not belong to the fish, but to some mammal. They look to me like a mammal's ears. It would be pretty hard to say what species of mammal, and almost impossible to determine what particular member of that species. They may merely be hysterical ears, in which case they will go away if you can get the fish's mind on something else.

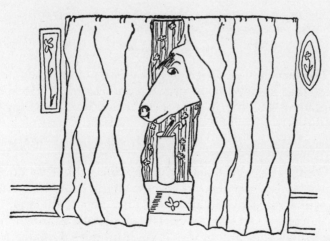

Q.   How would you feel if every time you looked up from your work or anything, here was a horse peering at you from behind something? He prowls about the house at all hours of the day and night. Doesn't seem worried about anything, merely wakeful. What should I do to discourage him?

MRS GRACE VOYNTON

A. The horse is probably sad. Changing the flowered decorations of your home to something less like open meadows might discourage him, but then I doubt whether it is a good idea to discourage a sad horse. In any case speak to him quietly when he turns up from behind things. Leaping at a horse in a house and crying 'Roogie, roogie!' or 'Whoosh!' would only result in breakage and bedlam. Of course you might finally get used to having him around, if the house is big enough for both of you.

Q. The fact that my dog sits this way so often leads me to believe that something is preying on his mind. He seems always to be studying. Would there be any way of finding out what this is?

ARTHUR

A. Owing to the artificially complex life led by city dogs of the present day, they tend to lose the simpler systems of intuition which once guided all breeds, and frequently lapse into what comes very close to mental perplexity. I myself have known some very profoundly thoughtful dogs. Usually, however, their problems are not serious and I should judge that your dog has merely mislaid something and wonders where he put it.

Q.   We have cats the way most people have mice.

MRS C. L. FOOTLOOSE

A.   I see you have. I can't tell from your communication, however, whether you wish advice or are just boasting.

Q.   No one has been able to tell us what kind of dog we have. I am enclosing a sketch of one of his two postures. He only has two. The other one is the same as this except he faces in the opposite direction.

    MRS EUGENIA BLACK

A.   I think that what you have is a cast-iron lawn dog. The expressionless eye and the rigid pose are characteristic of metal lawn animals. And that certainly is a cast-iron ear. You could, however, remove all doubt by means of a simple test with a hammer and a cold chisel, or an acetylene torch. If the animal chips, or melts, my diagnosis is correct.

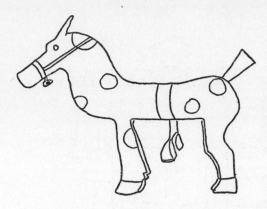

Q. My oldest boy, Ford Madox Ford Griswold, worked this wooden horse loose from a merry-go-round one night when he and some other young people were cutting up. Could you suggest any use for it in a family of five?

MRS R. L. S. GRISWOLD

A. I cannot try the patience of my public nor waste my own time dealing with the problems of insensate animals. Already I have gone perhaps too far afield in the case of stuffed birds and cast-iron lawn dogs. Pretty soon I should be giving advice on wire-haired fox terrier weather-vanes.

Q. Mr Jennings bought this beast when it was a pup in Montreal for a St Bernard, but I don't think it is. It's grown enormously and is stubborn about letting you have anything, like the bath towel it has its paws on, and the hat, both of which belong to Mr Jennings. He got it that bowling ball to play with but it doesn't seem to like it. Mr Jennings is greatly attached to the creature.

MRS FANNY EDWARDS JENNINGS

A.   What you have is a bear. While it isn't my bear, I should recommend that you dispose of it. As these animals grow older they get more and more adamant about letting you have anything, until finally there might not be anything in the house you could call your own – except possibly the bowling ball. Zoos use bears. Mr Jennings could visit it.

Q.   Sometimes my dog does not seem to know me. I think he must be crazy. He will draw away, or show his fangs, when I approach him.

H. M. MORGAN, JR

A.   So would I, and I'm not crazy. If you creep up on your dog the way you indicate in the drawing, I can understand his viewpoint. Put your shirt in and straighten up; you look as if you had never seen a dog before, and that is undoubtedly what bothers the animal. These maladjustments can often be worked out by the use of a little common sense.

23

Q.   After a severe storm we found this old male raven in the study of my father, the Hon. George Morton Bodwell, for many years head of the Latin Department at Tufts, sitting on a bust of Livy which was a gift to him from the class of '92. All that the old bird will say is 'Grawk'. Can ravens be taught to talk or was Poe merely 'romancing'?

MRS H. BODWELL COLWETHER

A. I am handicapped by an uncertainty as to who says 'Grawk', the raven or your father. It just happens that 'Arrk' is what ravens say. I have never known a raven that said anything but 'Arrk'.

Q. I have three Scotch terriers which take things out of closets and down from shelves, etc. My veterinarian advised me to gather together all the wreckage, set them down in the midst of it, and say 'ba-ad Scotties!' This, however, merely seems to give them a kind of pleasure. If I spank one, the other two jump me – playfully, but they jump me.

MRS O. S. PROCTOR

A. To begin with, I question the advisability of having three Scotch terriers. They are bound to get you down. However, it seems to me that you are needlessly complicating your own problem. The Scotties probably think that you are trying to enter into the spirit of their play. Their inability to comprehend what you are trying to get at will in the end make them melancholy, and you and the dogs will begin to drift further and further apart. I'd deal with each terrier, and each object, separately, beginning with the telephone, the disconnection of which must inconvenience you sorely.

Q.   My husband paid a hundred and seventy-five dollars for this moose to a man in Dorset, Ontario, who said he had trapped it in the woods. Something is wrong with his antlers, for we have to keep twisting them back into place all the time. They're loose.

MRS OLIPHANT BEATTY

A.   You people are living in a fool's paradise. The animal is obviously a horse with a span of antlers strapped on to his head. If you really want a moose, dispose of the horse; if you want to keep the horse, take the antlers off. Their constant pressure on his ears isn't a good idea.

MY LIFE AND HARD TIMES

Preface to a Life

Benvenuto Cellini said that a man should be at least forty years old before he undertakes so fine an enterprise as that of setting down the story of his life. He said also that an autobiographer should have accomplished something of excellence. Nowadays nobody who has a typewriter pays any attention to the old master's quaint rules. I myself have accomplished nothing of excellence except a remarkable and, to some of my friends, unaccountable expertness in hitting empty ginger ale bottles with small rocks at a distance of thirty paces. Moreover, I am not yet forty years old. But the grim date moves toward me apace; my legs are beginning to go, things blur before my eyes, and the faces of the rose-lipped maids I knew in my twenties are misty as dreams.

At forty my faculties may have closed up like flowers at evening, leaving me unable to write my memoirs with a fitting and discreet inaccuracy or, having written them, unable to carry them to the publisher's. A writer verging into the middle years lives in dread of losing his way to the publishing house and wandering down to the Bowery or the Battery, there to disappear like Ambrose Bierce. He has sometimes also the kindred dread of turning a sudden corner and meeting himself sauntering along in the opposite direction. I have known writers at this dangerous and tricky age to phone their homes from their offices, or their offices from their homes, ask for themselves in a low tone, and then, having fortunately discovered that they were 'out', to collapse in hard-breathing relief. This is particularly true of writers of light pieces running from a thousand to two thousand words.

The notion that such persons are gay of heart and carefree is curiously untrue. They lead, as a matter of fact, an existence of jumpiness and apprehension. They sit on the edge of the chair of Literature. In the house of Life they have the feeling that they have never taken off their overcoats. Afraid of losing themselves in the larger flight of the two-volume novel, or even the one-volume novel, they stick to short accounts of their misadventures because they never get so deep into them but that they feel they can get out. This type of writing is not a joyous form of self-expression but the manifestation of a twitchiness at once cosmic and mundane. Authors of such pieces have, nobody knows why, a genius for getting into minor difficulties: they walk into the wrong apartments, they drink furniture polish for stomach bitters, they drive their cars into the prize tulip beds of haughty neighbours, they playfully slap gangsters, mistaking them for old school friends. To call such persons 'humorists', a loose-fitting and ugly word, is to miss the nature of their dilemma and the dilemma of their nature. The little wheels of their invention are set in motion by the damp hand of melancholy.

Such a writer moves about restlessly wherever he goes, ready to get the hell out at the drop of a pie-pan or the lift of a skirt. His gestures are the ludicrous reflexes of the maladjusted; his repose is the momentary inertia of the nonplussed. He pulls the blinds against the morning and creeps into smokey corners at night. He talks largely about small matters and smally about great affairs. His ears are shut to the ominous rumblings of the dynasties of the world moving toward a cloudier chaos than ever before, but he hears with an acute perception the startling sounds that rabbits make twisting in the bushes along a country road at night and a cold chill comes upon him when the comic supplement of a Sunday newspaper blows unexpectedly out of an areaway and envelops his knees. He can sleep while the commonwealth crumbles but a strange sound in the pantry at three in the morning will strike terror into his stomach. He is not afraid, or much aware, of the menaces of empire but he keeps looking behind him as he walks along darkening streets out of the fear that he is being softly followed by little men padding along in single file, about a foot and a half high, large-eyed, and whiskered.

It is difficult for such a person to conform to what Ford Madox Ford in his book of recollections has called the sole reason for writing one's memoirs: namely, to paint a picture of one's time. Your short-piece writer's time is not Walter Lipp-mann's time, or Stuart Chase's time, or Professor Einstein's time. It is his own personal time, circumscribed by the short boundaries of his pain and his embarrassment, in which what happens to his digestion, the rear axle of his car, and the confused flow of his relationships with six or eight persons and two or three buildings is of greater importance than what goes on in the nation or in the universe. He knows vaguely that the nation is not much good any more; he has read that the crust of the earth is shrinking alarmingly and that the universe is growing steadily colder, but he does not believe that any of the three is in half as bad a shape as he is.

Enormous strides are made in star-measurement, theoretical economics, and the manufacture of bombing planes, but he usually doesn't find out about them until he picks up an old copy of *Time* on a picnic ground or in the summer house of a friend. He is aware that billions of dollars are stolen every year by bankers and politicians, and that thousands of people are out of work, but these conditions do not worry him a tenth as much as the conviction that he has wasted three months on a stupid psychoanalyst or the suspicion that a piece he has been working on for two long days was done much better and probably more quickly by Robert Benchley in 1924.

The 'time' of such a writer, then, is hardly worth reading about if the reader wishes to find out what was going on in the world while the writer in question was alive and at what might be laughingly called 'his best'. All that the reader is going to find out is what happened to the writer. The compensation, I suppose, must lie in the comforting feeling that one has had, after all, a pretty sensible and peaceful life, by comparison. It is unfortunate, however, that even a well-ordered life cannot lead anybody safely around the inevitable doom that waits in the skies. As F. Hopkinson Smith long ago pointed out, the claw of the sea-puss gets us all in the end.

J.T.

Sandy Hook, Connecticut,
25 September 1933.

The Night the Bed Fell

I suppose that the high-water mark of my youth in Columbus, Ohio, was the night the bed fell on my father. It makes a better recitation (unless, as some friends of mine have said, one has heard it five or six times) than it does a piece of writing, for it is almost necessary to throw furniture around, shake doors, and bark like a dog, to lend the proper atmosphere and verisimilitude to what is admittedly a somewhat incredible tale. Still, it did take place.

It happened, then, that my father had decided to sleep in the attic one night, to be away where he could think. My mother opposed the notion strongly because, she said, the old wooden bed up there was unsafe; it was wobbly and the heavy headboard would crash down on father's head in case the bed fell, and kill him. There was no dissuading him, however, and at a quarter past ten he closed the attic door behind him and went up the narrow twisting stairs. We later heard ominous creakings as he crawled into bed. Grandfather, who usually slept in the attic bed when he was with us, had disappeared some days before. (On these occasions he was usually gone six or eight days and returned growling and out of temper, with the news that the federal Union was run by a passel of blockheads and that the Army of the Potomac didn't have any more chance than a fiddler's bitch.)

We had visiting us at this time a nervous first cousin of mine named Briggs Beall, who believed that he was likely to cease breathing when he was asleep. It was his feeling that if he were not awakened every hour during the night, he might die of suffocation. He had been accustomed to setting an alarm clock to ring at intervals until morning, but I persuaded him to abandon this. He slept in my room and I told him that I was such a light sleeper that if anybody quit breathing in the same room with me, I would wake instantly. He tested me the first night – which I had suspected he would – by holding his breath after my regular breathing had convinced him I was asleep. I was not asleep, however, and called to him. This seemed to allay his fears a little, but he took the precaution of putting a glass of spirits of camphor on a little table at the head of his bed. In case

I didn't arouse him until he was almost gone, he said, he would sniff the camphor, a powerful reviver. Briggs was not the only member of his family who had his crotchets. Old Aunt Melissa Beall (who could whistle like a man, with two fingers in her mouth) suffered under the premonition that she was destined to die on South High Street, because she had been born on South High Street and married on South High Street. Then there was Aunt Sarah Shoaf, who never went to bed at night without the fear that a burglar was going to get in and blow chloroform under her door through a tube. To avert this calamity – for she was in greater dread of anaesthetics than of losing her household goods – she always piled her money, silverware, and other valuables in a neat stack just outside her bedroom, with a note reading: 'This is all I have. Please take it and do not use your chloroform, as this is all I have.' Aunt Gracie Shoaf also had a burglar phobia, but she met it with more fortitude. She was confident that burglars had been getting into her house every night for forty years. The fact that she never missed anything was to her no proof to the contrary. She always claimed that she scared them off before they could take anything, by throwing shoes down the hallway. When she went to bed she piled, where she could get at them handily, all the shoes there were about her house. Five minutes after she had turned off the light, she would sit up in bed and say 'Hark!' Her husband, who had learned to ignore the whole situation as long ago as 1903, would either be sound asleep or pretend to be sound asleep. In either case he would not respond to her tugging and pulling, so that presently she would arise, tiptoe to the door, open it slightly and heave a shoe down the hall in one direction, and its mate down the hall in the other direction. Some nights she threw them all, some nights only a couple of pairs.

But I am straying from the remarkable incidents that took place during the night that the bed fell on father. By midnight we were all in bed. The layout of the rooms and the disposition of their occupants is important to an understanding of what later occurred. In the front room upstairs (just under father's attic bedroom) were my mother and my brother Herman, who sometimes sang in his sleep, usually 'Marching Through Georgia' or 'Onward, Christian Soldiers'. Briggs Beall and myself

Some nights she threw them all

were in a room adjoining this one. My brother Roy was in a room across the hall from ours. Our bull terrier, Rex, slept in the hall.

My bed was an army cot, one of those affairs which are made wide enough to sleep on comfortably only by putting up, flat with the middle section, the two sides which ordinarily hang down like the sideboards of a drop-leaf table. When these sides are up, it is perilous to roll too far toward the edge, for then the cot is likely to tip completely over, bringing the whole bed down on top of one, with a tremendous banging crash. This, in fact, is precisely what happened, about two o'clock in the morning. (It was my mother who, in recalling the scene later, first referred to it as 'the night the bed fell on your father'.)

Always a deep sleeper, slow to arouse (I had lied to Briggs), I was at first unconscious of what had happened when the iron cot rolled me on to the floor and toppled over on me. It left me still warmly bundled up and unhurt, for the bed rested above me like a canopy. Hence I did not wake up, only reached the edge of consciousness and went back. The racket, however, instantly awakened my mother, in the next room, who came to the immediate conclusion that her worst dread was realised: the big wooden bed upstairs had fallen on father. She therefore screamed, 'Let's go to your poor father!' It was this shout, rather than the noise of my cot falling, that awakened Herman, in the same room with her. He thought that mother had become, for no apparent reason, hysterical. 'You're all right, Mamma!' he shouted, trying to calm her. They exchanged shout for shout for perhaps ten seconds: 'Let's go to your poor father!' and 'You're all right!' That woke up Briggs. By this time I was conscious of what was going on, in a vague way, but did not yet realise that I was under my bed instead of on it. Briggs, awakening in the midst of loud shouts of fear and apprehension, came to the quick conclusion that he was suffocating and that we were all trying to 'bring him out'. With a low moan, he

He came to the conclusion that he was suffocating

grasped the glass of camphor at the head of his bed and instead of sniffing it poured it over himself. The room reeked of camphor. 'Ugf, ahfg,' choked Briggs, like a drowning man, for he had almost succeeded in stopping his breath under the deluge of pungent spirits. He leaped out of bed and groped toward the open window, but he came up against one that was closed. With his hand, he beat out the glass, and I could hear it crash and tinkle on the alleyway below. It was at this juncture that I, in trying to get up, had the uncanny sensation of feeling my bed above me! Foggy with sleep, I now suspected, in my turn, that the whole uproar was being made in a frantic endeavour to extricate me from what must be an unheard-of and perilous situation. 'Get me out of this!' I bawled. 'Get me out!' I think I had the nightmarish belief that I was entombed in a mine. 'Gugh,' gasped Briggs, floundering in his camphor.

By this time my mother, still shouting, pursued by Herman, still shouting, was trying to open the door to the attic, in order to go up and get my father's body out of the wreckage. The door was stuck, however, and wouldn't yield. Her frantic pulls on it only added to the general banging and confusion. Roy and the dog were up, the one shouting questions, the other barking.

Father, furthest away and soundest sleeper of all, had by this time awakened by the battering on the attic door. He decided that the house was on fire. 'I'm coming, I'm coming!' he wailed in a slow, sleepy voice – it took him many minutes to regain full consciousness. My mother, still believing he was caught under the bed, detected in his 'I'm coming!' the mournful, resigned note of one who is preparing to meet his Maker. 'He's dying!' she shouted.

'I'm all right!' Briggs yelled to reassure her. 'I'm all right!' He still believed that it was his own closeness to death that was worrying mother. I found at last the light switch in my room, unlocked the door, and Briggs and I joined the others at the attic door. The dog, who never did like Briggs, jumped for him – assuming that he was the culprit in whatever was going on – and Roy had to throw Rex and hold him. We could hear father crawling out of bed upstairs. Roy pulled the attic door open, with a mighty jerk, and father came down the stairs, sleepy and irritable but safe and sound. My mother began to weep when

34

Roy had to throw Rex

she saw him. Rex began to howl. 'What in the name of God is going on here?' asked father.

The situation was finally put together like a gigantic jig-saw puzzle. Father caught a cold from prowling around in his bare feet but there were no other bad results. 'I'm glad', said mother, who always looked on the bright side of things, 'that your grandfather wasn't here.'

The Car We Had to Push

Many autobiographers, among them Lincoln Steffens and Gertrude Atherton, described earthquakes their families have been in. I am unable to do this because my family was never in an earthquake, but we went through a number of things in Columbus that were a great deal like earthquakes. I remember in particular some of the repercussions of an old Reo we had that wouldn't go unless you pushed it for quite a way and suddenly let your clutch out. Once, we had been able to start the engine easily by cranking it, but we had had the car for so many years that finally it wouldn't go unless you pushed it and let your clutch out. Of course, it took more than one person to do this; it took sometimes as many as five or six, depending on the grade of the roadway and conditions underfoot. The car was unusual in that the clutch and brake were on the same

35

It took sometimes as many as five or six

pedal, making it quite easy to stall the engine after it got
started, so that the car would have to be pushed again.

My father used to get sick at his stomach pushing the car, and
very often was unable to go to work. He had never liked the
machine, even when it was good, sharing my ignorance and
suspicion of all automobiles of twenty years ago and longer.
The boys I went to school with used to be able to identify every
car as it passed by: Thomas Flyer, Firestone-Columbus, Stevens
Duryea, Rambler, Winton, White Steamer, etc. I never could.
The only car I was really interested in was one that the Get-
Ready Man, as we called him, rode around town in: a big Red
Devil with a door in the back. The Get-Ready Man was a lank
unkempt elderly gentleman with wild eyes and a deep voice
who used to go about shouting at people through a megaphone
to prepare for the end of the world. 'GET READY! GET READY!'
he would bellow. 'THE WORLLLD IS COMING TO AN END!'
His startling exhortations would come up, like summer thunder, at the most unexpected times and in the most surprising
places. I remember once during Mantell's production of *King
Lear* at the Colonial Theatre, that the Get-Ready Man added his
bawlings to the squealing of Edgar and the ranting of the King
and the mouthing of the Fool, rising from somewhere in the
balcony to join in. The theatre was in absolute darkness and
there were rumblings of thunder and flashes of lightning off-
stage. Neither father nor I, who were there, ever completely got
over the scene, which went something like this:

36

The Get-Ready Man

EDGAR: Tom's a-cold. – O, do de do de, do de! – Bless thee from whirlwinds, star-blasting, and taking . . . the foul fiend vexes! (*Thunder off.*

LEAR: What! Have his daughters brought him to this pass? –

GET-READY MAN: Get ready! Get ready!

EDGAR: Pillicock sat on Pillocock-hill –

Halloo, halloo, loo, loo!

(*Lightning flashes*

GET-READY MAN: The Worllld is com-ing to an End!

FOOL: This cold night will turn us all to fools and madmen!

EDGAR: Take heed o' the foul fiend: obey thy paren—

GET-READY MAN: Get *Rea*-dy!

EDGAR: Tom's a-*cold*!

GET-READY MAN: The *Worr*-uld is coming to an end! . . .

They found him finally, and ejected him, still shouting. The Theatre, in our time, has known few such moments.

But to get back to the automobile. One of my happiest memories of it was when, in its eighth year, my brother Roy got together a great many articles from the kitchen, placed them in a square of canvas, and swung this under the car with a string attached to it so that, at a twitch, the canvas would give way and the steel and tin things would clatter to the street. This was a little scheme of Roy's to frighten father, who had always expected the car might explode. It worked perfectly. That was twenty-five years ago, but it is one of the few things in my life I would like to live over again if I could. I don't suppose that I can, now. Roy twitched the string in the middle of a lovely afternoon, on Bryden Road near Eighteenth Street. Father had closed his eyes and, with his hat off, was enjoying a cool breeze. The clatter on the asphalt was tremendously effective: knives, forks, can-openers, pie-pans, pot lids, biscuit-cutters, ladles, egg-beaters fell, beautifully together, in a lingering, clamant crash. 'Stop the *car*!' shouted father. 'I can't,' Roy said. 'The engine fell out.' 'God Almighty!' said father, who knew what *that* meant, or knew what it sounded as if it might mean.

It ended unhappily, of course, because we finally had to drive back and pick up the stuff and even father knew the difference between the works of an automobile and the equipment of a pantry. My mother wouldn't have known, however, nor *her* mother. My mother, for instance, thought – or, rather, knew – that it was dangerous to drive an automobile without gasoline: it fried the valves, or something: 'Now don't you dare drive all over town without gasoline!' she would say to us when we started off. Gasoline, oil, and water were much the same to her, a fact that made her life both confusing and perilous. Her greatest dread, however, was the Victrola – we had a very early one, back in the 'Come Josephine in My Flying Machine' days. She had an idea that the Victrola might blow up. It alarmed her, rather than reassured her, to explain that the phonograph was run neither by gasoline nor by electricity. She could only suppose that it was propelled by some newfangled and untested apparatus which was likely to let go at any minute, making us all the victims and martyrs of the wild-eyed Edison's dangerous experiments. The telephone she was comparatively at peace with, except, of course, during storms, when for some reason or other she always took the receiver off the hook and let it hang. She came naturally by her confused and groundless fears, for her own mother lived the latter years of her life in the horrible suspicion that electricity was dripping invisibly all over the house. It leaked, she contended, out of empty sockets if the wall switch had been left on. She would go around screwing in bulbs, and if they lighted up she would hastily and fearfully turn off the wall switch and go back to her *Pearson's* or *Everybody's*, happy in the satisfaction that she

Electricity was leaking all over the house

had stopped not only a costly but a dangerous leakage. Nothing could ever clear this up for her.

Our poor old Reo came to a horrible end, finally. We had parked it too far from the curb on a street with a car line. It was late at night and the street was dark. The first streetcar that came along couldn't get by. It picked up the tired old automobile as a terrier might seize a rabbit and drubbed it unmercifully, losing its hold now and then but catching a new grip a second later. Tyres booped and whooshed, the fenders queeled and graked, the steering wheel rose up like a spectre and disappeared in the direction of Franklin Avenue with a melancholy whistling sound, bolts and gadgets flew like sparks from a

Catherine wheel. It was a splendid spectacle but, of course, saddening to everybody (except the motorman of the streetcar, who was sore). I think some of us broke down and wept. It must have been the weeping that caused grandfather to take on so terribly. Time was all mixed up in his mind; automobiles and the like he never remembered having seen. He apparently gathered, from the talk and excitement and weeping, that somebody had died. Nor did he let go of this delusion. He insisted, in fact, after almost a week in which we strove mightily to divert him, that it was a sin and a shame and a disgrace on the family to put the funeral off any longer. 'Nobody is dead! The automobile is smashed!' shouted my father, trying for the thirtieth time to explain the situation to the old man. 'Was he drunk?' demanded grandfather, sternly. 'Was who drunk?' asked father. 'Zenas,' said grandfather. He had a name for the corpse now: it was his brother Zenas, who, as it happened, *was* dead, but not from driving an automobile while intoxicated. Zenas had died in 1866. A sensitive, rather poetical boy of twenty-one when the Civil War broke out, Zenas had gone to South America – 'just', as he wrote back, 'until it blows over'. Returning after the war had blown over, he caught the same disease that was killing off the chestnut trees in those years, and passed away. It was the only case in history where a tree doctor had to be called in to spray a person, and our family had felt it very keenly; nobody else in the United States caught the blight. Some of us have looked upon Zenas's fate as a kind of poetic justice.

Now that grandfather knew, so to speak, who was dead, it became increasingly awkward to go on living in the same house with him as if nothing had happened. He would go into towering rages in which he threatened to write to the Board of Health unless the funeral were held at once. We realised that something had to be done. Eventually, we persuaded a friend of father's, named George Martin, to dress up in the manner and costume of the eighteen-sixties and pretend to be Uncle Zenas, in order to set grandfather's mind at rest. The impostor looked fine and impressive in sideburns and a high beaver hat, and not unlike the daguerreotypes of Zenas in our album. I shall never forget the night, just after dinner, when this Zenas walked into the living-room. Grandfather was stomping up and down, tall, hawk-nosed, round-oathed. The newcomer held out both his

He caught the same disease that was killing the chestnut trees

hands. 'Clem!' he cried to grandfather. Grandfather turned slowly, looked at the intruder, and snorted. 'Who air *you*?' he demanded in his deep, resonant voice. 'I'm Zenas!' cried Martin. 'Your brother Zenas, fit as a fiddle and sound as a dollar!' 'Zenas, my foot!' said grandfather. 'Zenas died of the chestnut blight in '66!'

Grandfather was given to these sudden, unexpected, and extremely lucid moments; they were generally more embarrassing than his other moments. He comprehended before he went to bed that night that the old automobile had been destroyed and that its destruction had caused all the turmoil in the house. 'It flew all to pieces, Pa,' my mother told him, in graphically describing the accident. 'I knew 'twould,' growled grandfather. 'I allus told ye to git a Pope-Toledo.'

The Day the Dam Broke

My memories of what my family and I went through during the 1913 flood in Ohio I would gladly forget. And yet neither the hardships we endured nor the turmoil and confusion we experienced can alter my feeling toward my native state and city. I am having a fine time now and wish Columbus were here, but if anyone ever wished a city was in hell it was during that frightful and perilous afternoon in 1913 when the dam broke, or, to be more exact, when everybody in town thought that the dam broke. We were both ennobled and demoralised by the experience. Grandfather especially rose to magnificent heights which can never lose their splendour for me, even though his reactions to the flood were based upon a profound misconception; namely, that Nathan Bedford Forrest's cavalry was the menace we were called upon to face. The only possible means of escape for us was to flee the house, a step which grandfather sternly forbade, brandishing his old army sabre in his hand. 'Let the sons — — come!' he roared. Meanwhile hundreds of people were streaming by our house in wild panic, screaming 'Go east! Go east!' We had to stun grandfather with the ironing board. Impeded as we were by the inert form of the old gentleman – he was taller than six feet and weighed almost a hundred and seventy pounds – we were passed, in the first half-mile, by practically everybody else in the city. Had grandfather not come to, at the corner of Parsons Avenue and Town Street, we would unquestionably have been overtaken and engulfed by the roaring waters – that is, if there had *been* any roaring waters. Later, when the panic had died down and people had gone rather sheepishly back to their homes and their offices, minimising the distances they had run and offering various reasons for running, city engineers pointed out that even if the dam had broken, the water level would not have risen more than two additional inches in the West Side. The West Side was, at the time of the dam scare, under thirty feet of water – as, indeed, were all Ohio river towns during the great spring floods of twenty years ago. The East Side (where we lived and where all the running occurred) had never been in any danger at all. Only a rise of some ninety-five feet could have caused the flood waters to flow over High Street – the thoroughfare that divided the east side of town from the west – and engulf the East Side.

The fact that we were all as safe as kittens under a cookstove did not, however, assuage in the least the fine despair and the grotesque desperation which seized upon the residents of the East Side when the cry spread like a grass fire that the dam had given way. Some of the most dignified, staid, cynical, and clear-thinking men in town abandoned their wives, stenographers, homes, and offices and ran east. There are few alarms in the world more terrifying than 'The dam has broken!' There are few persons capable of stopping to reason when that clarion cry strikes upon their ears, even persons who live in towns no nearer than five hundred miles to a dam.

The Columbus, Ohio, broken-dam rumour began, as I recall it, about noon of 12 March 1913. High Street, the main canyon of trade, was loud with the placid hum of business and the buzzing of placid businessmen arguing, computing, wheed-ling, offering, refusing, compromising. Darius Conningway, one of the foremost corporation lawyers in the Middle-West, was telling the Public Utilities Commission in the language of Julius Caesar that they might as well try to move the Northern Star as to move him. Other men were making their little boasts and their gestures. Suddenly somebody began to run. It may be that he had simply remembered, all of a moment, an engage-ment to meet his wife, for which he was now frightfully late. Whatever it was, he ran east on Broad Street (probably toward the Maramor Restaurant, a favourite place for a man to meet his wife). Somebody else began to run, perhaps a newsboy in high spirits. Another man, a portly gentleman of affairs, broke into a trot. Inside of ten minutes, everybody on High Street from the Union Depot to the Courthouse was running. A loud mumble gradually crystallised into the dread word 'dam', 'The dam has broke!' The fear was put into words by a little old lady in an electric, or by a traffic cop, or by a small boy: no-body knows who, nor does it now really matter. Two thousand people were abruptly in full flight. 'Go east!' was the cry that arose – east away from the river, east to safety. 'Go east! Go east! Go east!'

43

Two thousand people were in full flight

Black streams of people flowed eastward down all the streets leading in that direction; these streams, whose headwaters were in the dry-goods stores, office buildings, harness shops, movie theatres, were fed by trickles of housewives, children, cripples, servants, dogs, and cats, slipping out of the houses past which the main streams flowed, shouting and screaming. People ran out leaving fires burning and food cooking and doors wide open. I remember, however, that my mother turned out all the fires and that she took with her a dozen eggs and two loaves of bread. It was her plan to make Memorial Hall, just two blocks away, and take refuge somewhere in the top of it, in one of the dusty rooms where war veterans met and where old battle flags and stage scenery were stored. But the seething throngs, shouting 'Go east!' drew her along and the rest of us with her. When grandfather regained full consciousness, at Parsons Avenue, he turned upon the retreating mob like a vengeful prophet and exhorted the men to form ranks and stand off the Rebel dogs, but at length he, too, got the idea that the dam had broken and, roaring 'Go east!' in his powerful voice, he caught up in one arm a small child and in the other a slight clerkish man of perhaps forty-two and we slowly began to gain on those ahead of us.

A scattering of firemen, policemen, and army officers in dress uniforms – there had been a review at Fort Hayes, in the northern part of town – added colour to the surging billows of people. 'Go east!' cried a little child in a piping voice, as she ran past a porch on which drowsed a lieutenant-colonel of infantry. Used to quick decisions, trained to immediate obedience, the officer bounded off the porch and, running at full tilt, soon passed the child, bawling 'Go east!' The two of them emptied rapidly the houses of the little street they were on. 'What is it? What is it?' demanded a fat, waddling man who intercepted the colonel. The officer dropped behind and asked the little child what it was. 'The dam has broke!' gasped the girl. 'The dam has broke!' roared the colonel. 'Go east! Go east! Go east!' He was soon leading, with the exhausted child in his arms, a fleeing company of three hundred persons who had gathered round him from living-rooms, shops, garages, backyards, and basements.

Nobody has ever been able to compute with an exactness how many people took part in the great rout of 1913, for the panic, which extended from the Winslow Bottling Works in the south end to Clintonville, six miles north, ended as abruptly as it began and the bobtail and ragtag and velvet-gowned groups of refugees melted away and slunk home, leaving the streets peaceful and deserted. The shouting, weeping, tangled evacuation of the city lasted not more than two hours in all. Some few people got as far east as Reynoldsburg, twelve miles away; fifty or more reached the Country Club, eight miles away; most of the others gave up, exhausted, or climbed trees in Franklin Park, four miles out. Order was restored and fear dispelled finally by means of militiamen riding about in motor lorries bawling through megaphones: 'The dam has *not* broken!' At first this tended only to add to the confusion and increase the panic, for many stampeders thought the soldiers were bellowing 'The dam has now broken!' thus setting an official seal of authentication on the calamity.

All the time, the sun shone quietly and there was nowhere any sign of oncoming waters. A visitor in an aeroplane, looking down on the straggling, agitated masses of people below, would have been hard put to it to divine a reason for the phenomenon. It must have inspired, in such an observer, a peculiar kind of terror, like the sight of the *Marie Celeste*, abandoned at sea, its galley fires peacefully burning, its tranquil decks bright in the sunlight.

An aunt of mine, Aunt Edith Taylor, was in a movie theatre on High Street when, over and above the sound of the piano in the pit (a W. S. Hart picture was being shown), there rose the steadily increasing tromp of running feet. Persistent shouts rose above the tromping. An elderly man, sitting near by aunt, mumbled something, got out of his seat, and went up the aisle at a dogtrot. This started everybody. In an instant the audience was jamming the aisles. 'Fire!' shouted a woman who always expected to be burned up in a theatre; but now the shouts outside were louder and coherent. 'The dam has broke!' cried somebody. 'Go east!' screamed a small woman in front of my aunt. And east they went, pushing and shoving and clawing, knocking women and children down, emerging finally into the street, torn and sprawling. Inside the theatre, Bill Hart was calmly calling some desperado's bluff and the brave girl at the piano played 'Row! Row! Row!' loudly and then 'In My Harem'. Outside, men were streaming across the Statehouse yard, others were climbing trees, a woman managed to get up on to the 'These Are My Jewels' statue, whose bronze figures of Sherman, Stanton, Grant, and Sheridan watched with cold unconcern the going to pieces of the capital city.

'I ran south to State Street, east on State to Third, south on Third to Town, and out east on Town,' my Aunt Edith has written me. 'A tall spare woman with grim eyes and a determined chin ran past me down the middle of the street. I was still uncertain as to what was the matter, in spite of all the shouting. I drew up alongside the woman with some effort, for although she was in her late fifties, she had a beautiful easy running form and seemed to be in excellent condition. "What is it?" I puffed. She gave me a quick glance and then looked ahead again, stepping up her pace a trifle. "Don't ask me, ask God!" she said.

'When I reached Grant Avenue, I was so spent that Dr H. R. Mallory – you remember Dr Mallory, the man with the white beard who looks like Robert Browning? – well, Dr Mallory, whom I had drawn away from at the corner of Fifth and Town,

'It's got us!' he shouted

passed me. "It's got us!" he shouted, and I felt sure that whatever it was *did* have us, for you know what conviction Dr Mallory's statements always carried. I didn't know at the time what he meant, but I found out later. There was a boy behind him on roller-skates, and Dr Mallory mistook the swishing of the skates for the sound of rushing water. He eventually reached the Columbus School for Girls, at the corner of Parsons Avenue and Town Street, where he collapsed, expecting the cold frothing waters of the Scioto to sweep him into oblivion. The boy on the skates swirled past him and Dr Mallory realised for the first time what he had been running from. Looking back up the street, he could see no signs of water, but nevertheless, after resting a few minutes, he jogged on east again. He caught up with me at Ohio Avenue, where we rested together. I should say that about seven hundred people passed us. A funny thing was that all of them were on foot. Nobody seemed to have had the courage to stop and start his car; but as I remember it, all cars had to be cranked in those days, which is probably the reason.'

The next day, the city went about its business as if nothing had happened, but there was no joking. It was two years or more before you dared treat the breaking of the dam lightly. And even now, twenty years after, there are a few persons, like Dr Mallory, who will shut up like a clam if you mention the Afternoon of the Great Run.

The Night the Ghost Got In

The ghost that got into our house on the night of 17 November 1915 raised such a hullabaloo of misunderstandings that I am sorry I didn't just let it keep on walking, and go to bed. Its advent caused my mother to throw a shoe through a window of the house next door and ended up with my grandfather shooting a patrolman. I am sorry, therefore, as I have said, that I ever paid any attention to the footsteps.

They began about a quarter past one o'clock in the morning, a rhythmic, quick-cadenced walking around the dining-room table. My mother was asleep in one room upstairs, my brother Herman in another; grandfather was in the attic, in the old walnut bed which, as you will remember, once fell on my father. I had just stepped out of the bathtub and was busily rubbing myself with a towel when I heard the steps. They were the steps of a man walking rapidly around the dining-room table downstairs. The light from the bathroom shone down the back steps, which dropped directly into the dining-room; I could see the faint shine of plates on the plate-rail; I couldn't see the table. The steps kept going round and round the table; at regular intervals a board creaked, when it was trod upon. I supposed at first that it was my father or my brother Roy, who had gone to Indianapolis but were expected home at any time. I suspected next that it was a burglar. It did not enter my mind until later that it was a ghost.

After the walking had gone on for perhaps three minutes, I tiptoed to Herman's room. 'Psst!' I hissed, in the dark, shaking him. 'Awp,' he said, in the low, hopeless tone of a despondent beagle – he always half suspected that something would 'get him' in the night. I told him who I was. 'There's something downstairs!' I said. He got up and followed me to the head of the back staircase. We listened together. There was no sound. The steps had ceased. Herman looked at me in some alarm; I had only the bath towel around my waist. He wanted to go back to bed, but I gripped his arm. 'There's something down there!' I said. Instantly the steps began again, circled the dining-room table like a man running, and started up the stairs toward us, heavily, two at a time. The light still shone palely down the

He always half suspected that something would get him

stairs; we saw nothing coming; we only heard the steps. Herman rushed to his room and slammed the door. I slammed shut the door at the stairs top and held my knee against it. After a long minute, I slowly opened it again. There was nothing there. There was no sound. None of us ever heard the ghost again.

The slamming of the doors had aroused mother: she peered out of her room. 'What on earth are you boys doing?' she demanded. Herman ventured out of his room. 'Nothing,' he said, gruffly, but he was, in colour, a light green. 'What was all that running around downstairs?' said mother. So she had heard the steps, too! We just looked at her. 'Burglars!' she shouted intuitively. I tried to quiet her by starting lightly downstairs.

'Come on, Herman,' I said.

'I'll stay with mother,' he said. 'She's all excited.'

I stepped back on to the landing.

'Don't either of you go a step,' said mother. 'We'll call the police.' Since the phone was downstairs, I didn't see how we were going to call the police – nor did I want the police – but mother made one of her quick, incomparable decisions. She flung up a window of her bedroom, which faced the bedroom windows of the house of a neighbour, picked up a shoe, and whammed it through a pane of glass across the narrow space that separated the two houses. Glass tinkled into the bedroom occupied by a retired engraver named Bodwell and his wife. Bodwell had been for some years in rather a bad way and was subject to mild 'attacks'. Most everybody we knew or lived near had *some* kind of attacks.

It was now about two o'clock of a moonless night; clouds hung black and low. Bodwell was at the window in a minute, shouting, frothing a little, shaking his fist. 'We'll sell the house and go back to Peoria,' we could hear Mrs Bodwell saying. It was some time before mother 'got through' to Bodwell. 'Burglars!' she shouted. 'Burglars in the house!' Herman and I hadn't dared to tell her that it was not burglars but ghosts, for she was even more afraid of ghosts than of burglars. Bodwell at first thought that she meant there were burglars in his house, but finally he quieted down and called the police for us over an extension phone by his bed. After he had disappeared from the window, mother suddenly made as if to throw another shoe, not because there was further need of it but, as she later explained, because the thrill of heaving a shoe through a window glass had enormously taken her fancy. I prevented her.

The police were on hand in a commendably short time: a Ford sedan full of them, two on motor-cycles, and a patrol wagon with about eight in it and a few reporters. They began banging at our front door. Flashlights shot streaks of gleam up and down the walls, across the yard, down the walk between our house and Bodwell's. 'Open up!' cried a hoarse voice. 'We're men from Headquarters!' I wanted to go down and let them in, since there they were, but mother wouldn't hear of it. 'You haven't a stitch on,' she pointed out. 'You'd catch your death.' I wound the towel around me again. Finally the cops put their shoulders to our big heavy front door with its thick bevelled glass and broke it in: I could hear a rending of wood and a splash of glass on the floor of the hall. Their lights played all over the living-room and criss-crossed nervously in the dining-room, stabbed into hallways, shot up the front stairs and finally up the back. They caught me standing in my towel at the top. A heavy policeman bounded up the steps. 'Who are

Police were all over the place

you?' he demanded. 'I live here,' I said. 'Well, whattsa matta, ya hot?' he asked. It was, as a matter of fact, cold; I went to my room and pulled on some trousers. On my way out, a cop stuck a gun into my ribs. 'Whatta you doin' here?' he demanded. 'I live here,' I said.

The officer in charge reported to mother. 'No sign of nobody, lady,' he said. 'Musta got away – whatt'd he look like?' 'There were two or three of them,' mother said, 'whooping and carrying on and slamming doors.' 'Funny,' said the cop. 'All ya windows and doors was locked on the inside tight as a tick.'

Downstairs, we could hear the tromping of the other police. Police were all over the place; doors were yanked open, drawers were yanked open, windows were shot up and pulled down, furniture fell with dull thumps. A half-dozen policemen emerged out of the darkness of the front hallway upstairs. They began to ransack the floor: pulled beds away from walls, tore clothes off hooks in the closets, pulled suitcases and boxes off shelves. One of them found an old zither that Roy had won in a pool tournament. 'Looky here, Joe,' he said strumming it with a big paw. The cop named Joe took it and turned it over. 'What is it?' he asked me. 'It's an old zither our guinea pig used to sleep on,' I said. It was true that a pet guinea pig we once had would never sleep anywhere except on the zither, but I should never have said so. Joe and the other cop looked at me a long time. They put the zither back on a shelf.

'No sign o' nuthin',' said the cop who had first spoken to mother. 'This guy', he explained to the others, jerking a thumb at me, 'was nekked. The lady seems historical.' They all nodded, but said nothing; just looked at me. In the small silence we all heard a creaking in the attic. Grandfather was turning over in bed. 'What's 'at?' snapped Joe. Five or six cops sprang for the attic door before I could intervene or explain. I realised that it would be bad if they burst in on grandfather unannounced or even announced. He was going through a phase in which he believed that General Meade's men, under steady hammering by Stonewall Jackson, were beginning to retreat and even desert.

When I got to the attic, things were pretty confused. Grandfather had evidently jumped to the conclusion that the police were deserters from Meade's army, trying to hide away in his attic. He bounded out of bed wearing a long flannel nightgown over long woollen underwear, a night-cap, and a leather jacket around his chest. The cops must have realised at once that the indignant white-haired old man belonged in the house, but they had no chance to say so. 'Back, ye cowardly dogs!' roared grandfather. 'Back t' the lines, ye goddam lily-livered cattle!' With that, he fetched the officer who found the zither a flat-handed smack along-side his head that sent him sprawling. The others beat a retreat, but not fast enough; grandfather grabbed Zither's gun from its holster and let fly. The report seemed to crack the rafters; smoke filled the attic. A cop cursed and shot his hand to his shoulder. Somehow, we all finally got downstairs again and locked the door against the old gentleman. He fired once or twice more in the darkness and then went back to bed. 'That was grandfather,' I explained to Joe, out of breath. 'He thinks you're deserters.' 'I'll say he does,' said Joe.

The cops were reluctant to leave without getting their hands on somebody besides grandfather; the night had been distinctly a defeat for them. Furthermore, they obviously didn't like the 'layout', something looked – and I can see their viewpoint – phony. They began to poke into things again. A reporter, a thin-faced, wispy man, came up to me. I had put on one of mother's blouses, not being able to find anything else. The reporter looked at me with mingled suspicion and interest. 'Just what the hell is the real lowdown here, Bud?' he asked. I decided to be frank with him. 'We had ghosts,' I said. He gazed at me a long time as if I were a slot machine into which he had, without results, dropped a nickel. Then he walked away. The cops followed him, the one grandfather shot holding his now-bandaged arm, cursing and blaspheming. 'I'm gonna get my gun back from that old bird,' said the zither-cop. 'Yeh,' said Joe. 'You – and who else?' I told them I would bring it to the station house the next day.

'What was the matter with that one policeman?' mother asked, after they had gone. 'Grandfather shot him,' I said. 'What for?' she demanded. I told her he was a deserter. 'Of all things!' said mother. 'He was such a nice-looking young man.'

Grandfather was fresh as a daisy and full of jokes at breakfast next morning. We thought at first he had forgotten all about what had happened, but he hadn't. Over his third cup of coffee, he glared at Herman and me. 'What was the idea of all them cops tarryhootin' round the house last night?' he demanded. He had us there.

More Alarms at Night

One of the incidents that I always think of first when I cast back over my youth is what happened the night that my father 'threatened to get Buck'. This, as you will see, is not precisely a fair or accurate description of what actually occurred, but it is the way in which I and the other members of my family invariably allude to the occasion. We were living at the time in an old house at 77 Lexington Avenue, in Columbus, Ohio. In the early years of the nineteenth century, Columbus won out, as state capital, by only one vote over Lancaster, and ever since then has had the hallucination that it is being followed, a curious municipal state of mind which affects, in some way or other, all those who live there. Columbus is a town in which almost anything is likely to happen and in which almost everything has.

My father was sleeping in the front room on the second floor next to that of my brother Roy, who was then about sixteen.

Father was usually in bed by nine-thirty and up again by ten-thirty to protest bitterly against a Victrola record we three boys were in the habit of playing over and over, namely 'No News, or What Killed the Dog', a recitation by Nat Wills. The record had been played so many times that its grooves were deeply cut and the needle often kept revolving in the same groove, repeating over and over the same words. Thus: 'ate some burnt hoss flesh, ate some burnt hoss flesh, ate some burnt hoss flesh'. It was this reiteration that generally got father out of bed.

On the night in question, however, we had all gone to bed at about the same time, without much fuss. Roy, as a matter of fact, had been in bed all day with a kind of mild fever. It wasn't severe enough to cause delirium and my brother was the last person in the world to give way to delirium. Nevertheless, he had warned father when father went to bed, that he *might* become delirious.

About three o'clock in the morning, Roy, who was wakeful, decided to pretend that delirium was on him, in order to have, as he later explained it, some 'fun'. He got out of bed and, going to my father's room, shook him and said, 'Buck, your time has come!' My father's name was not Buck but Charles, nor had he ever been called Buck. He was a tall, mildly nervous, peaceable gentleman, given to quiet pleasures, and eager that everything should run smoothly. 'Hmm?' he said, with drowsy bewilderment. 'Get up, Buck,' said my brother, coldly, but with a certain gleam in his eyes. My father leaped out of bed, on the side away from his son, rushed from the room, locked the door behind him, and shouted us all up.

We were naturally reluctant to believe that Roy, who was quiet and self-contained, had threatened his father with any such abracadabra as father said he had. My older brother, Herman, went back to bed without any comment. 'You've had a bad dream,' my mother said. This vexed my father. 'I tell you he called me Buck and told me my time had come,' he said. We went to the door of his room, unlocked it, and tiptoed through it to Roy's room. He lay in his bed, breathing easily, as if he were fast asleep. It was apparent at a glance that he did not have a high fever. My mother gave my father a look. 'I tell you he did,' whispered father.

Our presence in the room finally seemed to awaken Roy and

he was (or rather, as we found out long afterward, pretended to be) astonished and bewildered. 'What's the matter?' he asked. 'Nothing,' said my mother. 'Just your father had a nightmare.' 'I did not have a nightmare,' said father, slowly and firmly. He wore an old-fashioned, 'side-slit' nightgown which looked rather odd on his tall, spare figure. The situation, before we let it drop and everybody went back to bed again, became, as such situations in our family usually did, rather more complicated than ironed out. Roy demanded to know what had happened, and my mother told him, in considerably garbled fashion, what father had told her. At this a light dawned in Roy's eyes. 'Dad's got it backward,' he said. He then explained that he had heard father get out of bed and had called to him. 'I'll handle this,' his father had answered. 'Buck is downstairs.' 'Who is this Buck?' my mother demanded of father. 'I don't know any Buck and I never said that,' father contended, irritably. None of us (except Roy, of course) believed him. 'You had a dream,' said mother. 'People have these dreams.' 'I did not have a dream,' father said. He was pretty well nettled by this time, and he stood in front of a bureau mirror, brushing his hair with a pair of military brushes; it always seemed to calm father to brush his hair. My mother declared that it was 'a sin and a shame' for a grown man to wake up a sick boy simply because he (the grown man: father) had got on his back and had a bad dream. My father, as a matter of fact, *had* been known to have nightmares, usually about Lillian Russell and President Cleveland, who chased him.

We argued the thing for perhaps another half-hour, after which mother made father sleep in her room. 'You're all safe now, boys,' she said, firmly, as she shut her door. I could hear father grumbling for a long time, with an occasional monosyllable of doubt from mother.

It was some six months after this that father went through a similar experience with me. He was at that time sleeping in the room next to mine. I had been trying all afternoon, in vain, to think of the name Perth Amboy. It seems now like a very simple name to recall and yet on the day in question I thought of every other town in the country, as well as such words and names and phrases as terra cotta, Walla-Walla, bill of lading, vice versa, hoity-toity, Pall Mall, Bodley Head, Schumann-

Heink, etc., without even coming close to Perth Amboy. I suppose terra cotta was the closest I came, although it was not very close.

Long after I had gone to bed, I was struggling with the problem. I began to indulge in the wildest fancies as I lay there in the dark, such as that there was no such town, and even that there was no such state as New Jersey. I fell to repeating the word 'Jersey' over and over again, until it became idiotic and meaningless. If you have ever lain awake at night and repeated one word over and over, thousands and millions and hundreds of thousands of millions of times, you know the disturbing mental state you can get into. I got to thinking that there was nobody else in the world but me, and various other wild imaginings of that nature. Eventually, lying there thinking these outlandish thoughts, I grew slightly alarmed. I began to suspect that one might lose one's mind over some such trivial mental tic as a futile search for terra firma Piggly Wiggly Gorgonzola Prester John Arc de Triomphe Holy Moses Lares and Penates. I began to feel the imperative necessity of human contact. This silly and alarming tangle of thought and fancy had gone far enough. I might get into some kind of mental aberrancy unless I found out the name of that Jersey town and could go to sleep. Therefore, I got out of bed, walked into the room where father was sleeping, and shook him. 'Um!' he mumbled. I shook him more fiercely and he finally woke up, with a glaze of dream and apprehension in his eyes. 'What's matter?' he asked, thickly. I must, indeed, have been rather wild of eye, and my hair, which is unruly, becomes monstrously tousled and snarled at night. 'Wha's it?' said my father, sitting up, in readiness to spring out of bed on the far side. The thought must have been going through his mind that all his sons were crazy, or on the verge of going crazy. I see that now, but I didn't then, for I had forgotten the Buck incident and did not realise how similar my appearance must have been to Roy's the night he called father Buck and told him his time had come. 'Listen,' I said. 'Name some towns in New Jersey quick!' It must have been around three in the morning. Father got up, keeping the bed between him and me, and started to pull his trousers on. 'Don't bother about dressing,' I said. 'Just name some towns in New Jersey.' While he hastily pulled on his clothes – I remember he left his socks off and put his shoes on his bare feet – father began to name, in a shaky voice, various New Jersey cities. I can still see him reaching for his coat without taking his eyes off me. 'Newark,' he said, 'Jersey City, Atlantic City, Elizabeth, Paterson, Passaic, Trenton, Jersey City, Trenton, Paterson—' 'It has two names,' I snapped. 'Elizabeth and Paterson,' he said. 'No, no!' I told him, irritably. 'This is one town with one name, but there are two words in it, like helter-skelter.' 'Helter-skelter,' said my father, moving slowly toward the bedroom door and smiling in a faint, strained way which I understand now – but didn't then – was meant to humour me. When he was within a few paces of the door, he fairly leaped for it and ran out into the hall, his coat-tails and shoelaces flying. The exit stunned me. I had no notion that he thought I had gone out of my senses; I could only believe that he had gone out of *his* or that, only partially awake, he was engaged in some form of running in his sleep. I ran after him and I caught him at the door of mother's room and grabbed him, in order to reason with him. I shook him a little, thinking to wake him completely. 'Mary! Roy! Herman!' he shouted. I, too, began to shout for my brothers and my mother. My mother opened her door instantly, and there we were at 3.30 in the morning grappling and shouting, father partly dressed, but without socks or shirt, and I in pyjamas.

'*Now*, what?' demanded my mother, grimly, pulling us apart. She was capable, fortunately, of handling any two of us and she never in her life was alarmed by the words or actions of any one of us.

'Look out for Jamie!' said father. (He always called me Jamie when excited.) My mother looked at me.

'What's the matter with your father?' she demanded. I said I didn't know; I said he had got up suddenly and dressed and ran out of the room.

'Where did you think you were going?' mother asked him, coolly. He looked at me. We looked at each other, breathing hard, but somewhat calmer.

'He was babbling about New Jersey at this infernal hour of the night,' said father. 'He came to my room and asked me to name towns in New Jersey.' Mother looked at me.

'I just asked him,' I said. 'I was trying to think of one and couldn't sleep.'

'You see?' said father, triumphantly. Mother didn't look at him.

'Get to bed, both of you,' she said. 'I don't want to hear any more out of you tonight. Dressing and tearing up and down the hall at this hour in the morning!' She went back into the room and shut her door. Father and I went back to bed. 'Are you all right?' he called to me. 'Are you?' I asked. 'Well, good night,' he said. 'Good night,' I said.

Mother would not let the rest of us discuss the affair next morning at breakfast. Herman asked what the hell had been the matter. 'We'll go on to something more elevating,' said mother.

A Sequence of Servants

When I look back on the long line of servants my mother hired during the years I lived at home, I remember clearly ten or twelve of them (we had about a hundred and sixty-two, all told, but few of them were memorable). There was, among the immortals, Dora Gedd, a quiet, mousy girl of thirty-two who one night shot at a man in her room, throwing our household into an uproar that was equalled perhaps only by the goings-on the night the ghost got in. Nobody knew how her lover, a morose garage man, got into the house, but everybody for two blocks knew how he got out. Dora had dressed up in a lavender evening gown for the occasion and she wore a mass of jewellery, some of which was my mother's. She kept shouting something from Shakespeare after the shooting – I forget just what – and pursued the gentleman downstairs from her attic room. When he got to the second floor he rushed into my father's room. It was this entrance, and not the shot or the shouting, that aroused father, a deep sleeper always. 'Get me out of here!' shouted the victim. This situation rapidly developed, from then on, into one of those bewildering involvements for which my family had, I am afraid, a kind of unhappy genius. When the cops arrived Dora was shooting out the Welsbach gas mantles in the living-room, and her gentleman friend had fled. By dawn everything was quiet once more.

There were others. Gertie Straub: big, genial, and ruddy, a collector of pints of rye (we learned after she was gone), who came in after two o'clock one night from a dancing party at Buckeye Lake and awakened us by bumping into and knocking over furniture. 'Who's down there?' called mother from upstairs. 'It's me, dearie,' said Gertie, 'Gertie Straub.' 'What are you *doing*?' demanded mother. 'Dusting,' said Gertie.

'Dusting,' said Gertie

Juanemma Kramer was one of my favourites. Her mother loved the name Juanita so dearly that she had worked the first part of it into the names of all her daughters – they were (in addition to a Juanita) Juanemma, Juanhelen, and Juangrace. Juanemma was a thin, nervous maid who lived in constant dread of being hypnotised. Nor were her fears unfounded, for she was so extremely susceptible to hypnotic suggestion that

59

one evening at B. F. Keith's theatre when a man on the stage was hypnotised, Juanemma, in the audience, was hypnotised too and floundered out into the aisle making the same cheeping sound that the subject on the stage, who had been told he was a chicken, was making. The act was abandoned and some xylophone players were brought on to restore order. One night, when our house was deep in quiet slumber, Juanemma became hypnotised in her sleep. She dreamed that a man 'put her under' and then disappeared without 'bringing her out'. This was explained when, at last, a police surgeon whom we called in – he was the only doctor we could persuade to come out at three in the morning – slapped her into consciousness. It got so finally that any buzzing or whirling sound or any flashing object would put Juanemma under, and we had to let her go. I was reminded of her recently when, at a performance of the movie *Rasputin and the Empress*, there came the scene in which Lionel Barrymore as the unholy priest hypnotises the Czarevitch by spinning before his eyes a glittering watch. If Juanemma sat in any theatre and witnessed that scene she must, I am sure, have gone under instantly. Happily, she seems to have missed the picture, for otherwise Mr Barrymore might have had to dress up again as Rasputin (which God forbid) and journey across the country to get her out of it – excellent publicity but a great bother.

Before I go on to Vashti, whose last name I forget, I will look in passing at another of our white maids (Vashti was coloured). Belle Giddin distinguished herself by one gesture which fortunately did not result in the bedlam occasioned by Juanemma's hypnotic states or Dora Gedd's shooting spree. Bella burned her finger grievously, and purposely, one afternoon in the steam of a boiling kettle so that she could find out whether the pain-killer she had bought one night at a tent-show for fifty cents was any good. It was only fair.

Vashti turned out, in the end, to be partly legendary. She was a comely and sombre Negress who was always able to find things my mother lost. 'I don't know what's become of my garnet brooch,' my mother said one day. 'Yassum,' said Vashti. In half an hour she had found it. 'Where in the world was it?' asked mother. 'In de yahd,' said Vashti. 'De dog mussa drug it out.'

Vashti was in love with a young coloured chauffeur named Charley, but she was also desired by her stepfather, whom none of us had ever seen but who was, she said, a handsome but messin' round gentleman from Georgia who had come north and married Vashti's mother just so he could be near Vashti. Charley, her fiancé, was for killing the stepfather but we counselled flight to another city. Vashti, however, would burst into tears and hymns and vow she'd never leave us; she got a certain pleasure out of bearing her cross. Thus we all lived in jeopardy, for the possibility that Vashti, Charley, and her stepfather might fight it out some night in our kitchen did not, at times, seem remote. Once I went into the kitchen at midnight to make some coffee. Charley was standing at a window looking out into the backyard; Vashti was rolling her eyes. 'Heah he come! Heah he come!' she moaned. The stepfather didn't show up, however.

Charley finally saved up twenty-seven dollars toward taking Vashti away but one day he impulsively bought a .22 revolver with a mother-of-pearl handle and demanded that Vashti tell him where her mother and stepfather lived. 'Doan go up dere, doan go *up* dere!' said Vashti. 'Mah mothah is just as rarin' as he is!' Charley, however, insisted. It came out then that Vashti didn't have any stepfather; there was no such person. Charley threw her over for a yellow gal named Nancy: he never forgave Vashti for the vanishing from his life of a menace that had come to mean more to him than Vashti herself. Afterwards, if you asked Vashti about her stepfather or about Charley she would say, proudly, and with a woman-of-the-world air, 'Neither one ob'em is messin' round *me* any mo'.'

Mrs Doody, a huge, middle-aged woman with a religious taint, came into and went out of our house like a comet. The second night she was there she went berserk while doing the dishes and, under the impression that father was the Antichrist, pursued him several times up the backstairs and down the front. He had been sitting quietly over his coffee in the living-room when she burst in from the kitchen waving a bread knife. My brother Herman finally felled her with a piece of Libby's cut-glass that had been a wedding present of mother's. Mother, I remember, was in the attic at the time, trying to find some old things, and, appearing on the scene in the

One night while doing the dishes . . .

midst of it all, got the quick and mistaken impression that father was chasing Mrs Doody.

Mrs Robertson, a fat and mumbly old coloured woman, who might have been sixty and who might have been a hundred, gave us more than one turn during the many years that she did our washing. She had been a slave down South and she remembered 'having seen the troops marching – a mess o' blue, den a mess o' grey'. 'What', my mother asked her once, 'were they fighting about?' 'Dat', said Mrs Robertson, 'Ah don't know.' She had a feeling, at all times, that something was going to happen. I can see her now, staggering up from the basement with a basketful of clothes and coming abruptly to a halt in the middle of the kitchen. 'Hahk!' she would say, in a deep, guttural voice.

We would all hark; there was never anything to be heard. Neither, when she shouted 'Look yondah!' and pointed a trembling hand at a window, was there ever anything to be seen. Father protested time and again that he couldn't stand Mrs Robertson around, but mother always refused to let her go. It seems that she was a jewel. Once she walked unbidden, a dishpan full of wrung-out clothes under her arm, into father's study, where he was engrossed in some figures. Father looked up. She regarded him for a moment in silence. Then – 'Look out!' she said, and withdrew. Another time, a murky winter afternoon, she came flubbering up the cellar stairs and bounced, out of breath, into the kitchen. Father was in the kitchen sipping some black coffee; he was in a jittery state of nerves from the effects of having had a tooth out, and had been in bed most of the day. 'Dey is a death watch downstaihs!' rumbled the old coloured lady. It developed that she had heard a strange 'chipping' noise back of the furnace. 'That was a cricket,' said father. 'Um-*hm*,' said Mrs Robertson. 'Dat was uh death watch!' With that she put on her hat and went home, poising just long enough at the back door to observe darkly to father, '*Dey ain't no way!*' It upset him for days.

Mrs Robertson had only one great hour that I can think of – Jack Johnson's victory over Mistah Jeffries on the Fourth of July, 1910. She took a prominent part in the coloured parade through the South End that night, playing a Spanish fandango on a banjo. The procession was led by the pastor of her church who, Mrs Robertson later told us, had 'splained that the victory of Jack over Mistah Jeffries proved 'de 'speriority ob de race'.

'What', asked my mother, 'did he mean by that?' 'Dat', said Mrs Robertson, 'Ah don't know.'

Our other servants I don't remember so clearly, except the one who set the house on fire (her name eludes me), and Edda Millmoss. Edda was always slightly morose but she had gone along for months, all the time she was with us, quietly and efficiently attending to her work, until the night we had Carson Blair and F. R. Gardiner to dinner – both men of importance to my father's ambitions. Then, suddenly, while serving the entrée, Edda dropped everything and, pointing a quivering finger at father, accused him in a long rigamarole of having done her out of her rights to the land on which Trinity Church in New York stands. Mr Gardiner had one of his 'attacks' and the whole evening turned out miserably.

The Dog that Bit People

Probably no one man should have as many dogs in his life as I have had, but there was more pleasure than distress in them for me except in the case of an Airedale named Muggs. He gave me more trouble than all the other fifty-four or -five put together, although my moment of keenest embarrassment was the time a Scotch terrier named Jeannie, who had just had six puppies in the clothes closet of a fourth floor apartment in New York, had the unexpected seventh and last at the corner of Eleventh Street and Fifth Avenue during a walk she had insisted on taking. Then, too, there was the prize-winning French poodle, a great big black poodle – none of your little, untroublesome white miniatures – who got sick riding in the rumble seat of a car with me on her way to the Greenwich Dog Show. She had a red rubber bib tucked around her throat and, since a rain storm came up when we were half way through the Bronx, I had to hold over her a small green umbrella, really more of a parasol. The rain beat down fearfully and suddenly the driver of the car drove into a big garage, filled with mechanics. It happened so quickly that I forgot to put the umbrella down and I will always remember, with sickening distress, the look of incredulity mixed with hatred that came over the face of the particular hardened garage man that came over to see what we wanted, when he took a look at me and the poodle. All garage men, and people of that intolerant stripe, hate poodles with their curious haircut, especially the pom-poms that you got to leave on their hips if you expect the dogs to win a prize.

But the Airedale, as I have said, was the worst of all my dogs. He really wasn't my dog, as a matter of fact: I came home from a vacation one summer to find that my brother Roy had bought him while I was away. A big, burly, choleric dog, he always acted as if he thought I wasn't one of the family. There was a slight advantage in being one of the family, for he didn't bite the family as often as he bit strangers. Still, in the years that we had him he bit everybody but mother, and he made a pass at her once but missed. That was during the month when we suddenly had mice, and Muggs refused to do anything about them. Nobody ever had mice exactly like the mice we had that month. They acted like pet mice, almost like mice somebody had trained. They were so friendly that one night when mother entertained at dinner the Friraliras, a club she and my father had belonged to for twenty years, she put down a lot of little dishes with food in them on the pantry floor so that the mice would be satisfied with that and wouldn't come into the dining-room. Muggs stayed out in the pantry with the mice, lying on the floor, growling to himself – not at the mice, but about all the people in the next room that he would have liked to get at. Mother slipped out into the pantry once to see how everything was going. Everything was going fine. It made her so mad to see Muggs lying there, oblivious of the mice – they came running up to her – that she slapped him and he slashed at her, but didn't make it. He was sorry immediately, mother said. He was always sorry, she said, after he bit someone, but we could not understand how she figured this out. He didn't act sorry.

Mother used to send a box of candy every Christmas to the people the Airedale bit. The list finally contained forty or more names. Nobody could understand why we didn't get rid of the dog. I didn't understand it very well myself, but we didn't get rid of him. I think that one or two people tried to poison Muggs – he acted poisoned once in a while – and old Major Moberly fired at him once with his service revolver near the Seneca Hotel in East Broad Street – but Muggs lived to be almost eleven years old and even when he could hardly get around he bit a Congressman who had called to see my father on business. My mother had never liked the Congressman – she said the signs of his horoscope showed he couldn't be trusted (he was Saturn with the moon in Virgo) – but she sent him a box of candy that Christmas. He sent it right back, probably because he suspected it was trick candy. Mother persuaded herself it was all for the best that the dog had bitten him, even though father lost an important business association because of it. 'I wouldn't be associated with such a man,' mother said. 'Muggs could read him like a book.'

We used to take turns feeding Muggs to be on his good side,

Nobody knew exactly what was the matter with him

but that didn't always work. He was never in a very good
humour, even after a meal. Nobody knew exactly what was the
matter with him, but whatever it was it made him irascible,
especially in the mornings. Roy never felt very well in the
morning, either, especially before breakfast, and once when he
came downstairs and found that Muggs had moodily chewed
up the morning paper he hit him in the face with a grapefruit
and then jumped up on the dining-room table, scattering
dishes and silverware and spilling the coffee. Muggs' first free
leap carried him all the way across the table and into a brass fire
screen in front of the gas grate but he was back on his feet in a
moment and in the end he got Roy and gave him a pretty
vicious bite in the leg. Then he was all over it; he never bit anyone more than once at a time. Mother always mentioned that
as an argument in his favour; she said he had a quick temper
but that he didn't hold a grudge. She was forever defending
him. I think she liked him because he wasn't well. 'He's not
strong,' she would say, pityingly, but that was inaccurate; he
may not have been well but he was terribly strong.

One time my mother went to the Chittenden Hotel to call on
a woman mental healer who was lecturing in Columbus on the
subject of 'Harmonious Vibrations'. She wanted to find out if it
was possible to get harmonious vibrations into a dog. 'He's a
large tan-coloured Airedale,' mother explained. The woman

said that she had never treated a dog but she advised my mother to hold the thought that he did not bite and would not bite. Mother was holding the thought the very next morning when Muggs got the iceman but she blamed that slip-up on the iceman. 'If you didn't think he would bite you, he wouldn't,' mother told him. He stomped out of the house in a terrible jangle of vibrations.

One morning when Muggs bit me slightly, more or less in passing, I reached down and grabbed his short stumpy tail and hoisted him into the air. It was a foolhardy thing to do and the last time I saw my mother, about six months ago, she said she didn't know what possessed me. I don't either, except that I was pretty mad. As long as I held the dog off the floor by his tail he couldn't get at me, but he twisted and jerked so, snarling all the time, that I realised I couldn't hold him that way very long. I carried him to the kitchen and flung him on to the floor and shut the door on him just as he crashed against it. But I forgot about the backstairs. Muggs went up the backstairs and down the frontstairs and had me cornered in the living-room. I managed to get up on to the mantelpiece above the fireplace, but it gave way and came down with a tremendous crash throwing a large marble clock, several vases, and myself heavily to the floor. Muggs was so alarmed by the racket that when I picked myself up he had disappeared. We couldn't find him anywhere, although we whistled and shouted, until old Mrs Detweiler called after dinner that night. Muggs had bitten her once, in the leg, and she came into the living-room only after we assured her that Muggs had run away. She had just seated herself when, with a great growling and scratching of claws, Muggs emerged from under a davenport where he had been quietly hiding all the time, and bit her again. Mother examined the bite and put arnica on it and told Mrs Detweiler that it was only a bruise. 'He just bumped you,' she said. But Mrs Detweiler left the house in a nasty state of mind.

Lots of people reported our Airedale to the police but my father held a municipal office at the time and was on friendly terms with the police. Even so, the cops had been out a couple of times – once when Muggs bit Mrs Rufus Sturtevant and again when he bit Lieutenant-Governor Malloy – but mother told them that it hadn't been Muggs' fault but the fault of the

Lots of people reported our dog to the police

people who were bitten. 'When he starts for them, they scream,' she explained, 'and that excites him.' The cops suggested that it might be a good idea to tie the dog up, but mother said that it mortified him to be tied up and that he wouldn't eat when he was tied up.

Muggs at his meals was an unusual sight. Because of the fact that if you reached toward the floor he would bite you, we usually put his food plate on top of an old kitchen table with a bench alongside the table. Muggs would stand on the bench and eat. I remember that my mother's Uncle Horatio, who boasted that he was the third man up Missionary Ridge, was splutteringly indignant when he found out that we fed the dog on a table because we were afraid to put his plate on the floor. He said he wasn't afraid of any dog that ever lived and that he would put the dog's plate on the floor if we would give it to him. Roy said that if Uncle Horatio had fed Muggs on the ground just before the battle he would have been the first man up Missionary Ridge. Uncle Horatio was furious. 'Bring him in! Bring him in now!' he shouted. 'I'll feed the —— on the floor!' Roy was all for giving him a chance, but my father

Muggs at his meals was an unusual sight

wouldn't hear of it. He said that Muggs had already been fed.
'I'll feed him again!' bawled Uncle Horatio. We had quite a time
quieting him.

In his last year Muggs used to spend practically all of his
time outdoors. He didn't like to stay in the house for some reason or other – perhaps it held too many unpleasant memories
for him. Anyway, it was hard to get him to come in and as a
result the garbage man, the iceman, and the laundryman
wouldn't come near the house. We had to haul the garbage
down to the corner, take the laundry out and bring it back, and
meet the iceman a block from home. After this had gone on for
some time we hit on an ingenious arrangement for getting the
dog in the house so that we could lock him up while the gas
meter was read, and so on. Muggs was afraid of only one thing,
an electrical storm. Thunder and lightning frightened him out
of his senses (I think he thought a storm had broken the day
the mantelpiece fell). He would rush into the house and hide
under a bed or in a clothes closet. So we fixed up a thunder machine out of a long narrow piece of sheet iron with a wooden
handle on one end. Mother would shake this vigorously when

she wanted to get Muggs into the house. It made an excellent imitation of thunder, but I suppose it was the most roundabout system for running a household that was ever devised. It took a lot out of mother.

A few months before Muggs died, he got to 'seeing things'. He would rise slowly from the floor, growling low, and stalk stiff-legged and menacing toward nothing at all. Sometimes the Thing would be just a little to the right or left of a visitor. Once a Fuller Brush salesman got hysterics. Muggs came wandering into the room like Hamlet following his father's ghost. His eyes were fixed on a spot just to the left of the Fuller Brush man, who stood it until Muggs was about three slow, creeping paces from him. Then he shouted. Muggs wavered on past him into the hallway grumbling to himself but the Fuller man went on shouting. I think mother had to throw a pan of cold water on him before he stopped. That was the way she used to stop us boys when we got into fights.

Muggs died quite suddenly one night. Mother wanted to bury him in the family lot under a marble stone with some such inscription as 'Flights of angels sing thee to thy rest' but we persuaded her it was against the law. In the end we just put up a smooth board above his grave along a lonely road. On the board I wrote with an indelible pencil 'Cave Canem'. Mother was quite pleased with the simple classic dignity of the old Latin epitaph.

University Days

I passed all the other courses that I took at my University, but I could never pass botany. This was because all botany students had to spend several hours a week in a laboratory looking through a microscope at plant cells, and I could never see through a microscope. I never once saw a cell through a microscope. This used to enrage my instructor. He would wander around the laboratory pleased with the progress all the students were making in drawing the involved and, so I am told, interesting structure of flower cells, until he came to me. I would just be standing there. 'I can't see anything,' I would say. He would begin patiently enough, explaining how anybody can see through a microscope, but he would always end up in a fury, claiming that I could *too* see through a microscope but just pretended that I couldn't. 'It takes away from the beauty of flowers anyway,' I used to tell him. 'We are not concerned with beauty in this course,' he would say. 'We are concerned solely with what I may call the *mechanics* of flars.' 'Well,' I'd say, 'I can't see anything.' 'Try it just once again,' he'd say, and I would put my eye to the microscope and see nothing at all, except now and again a nebulous milky substance – a phenomenon of maladjustment. You were supposed to see a vivid, restless clockwork of sharply defined plant cells. 'I see what looks like a lot of milk,' I would tell him. This, he claimed, was the result of my not having adjusted the microscope properly, so he would readjust it for me, or rather, for himself. And I would look again and see milk.

I finally took a deferred pass, as they called it, and waited a year and tried again. (You had to pass one of the biological sciences or you couldn't graduate.) The professor had come back from vacation brown as a berry, bright-eyed, and eager to explain cell-structure again to his classes. 'Well,' he said to me, cheerily, when we met in the first laboratory hour of the semester, 'we're going to see cells this time, aren't we?' 'Yes, sir,' I said. Students to right of me and to left of me and in front of me were seeing cells; what's more, they were quietly drawing pictures of them in their notebooks. Of course, I didn't see anything.

'We'll try it', the professor said to me, grimly, 'with every adjustment of the microscope known to man. As God is my witness, I'll arrange this glass so that you see cells through it or I'll give up teaching. In twenty-two years of botany, I—' He cut off abruptly for he was beginning to quiver all over, like Lionel Barrymore, and he genuinely wished to hold on to his temper; his scenes with me had taken a great deal out of him.

So we tried it with every adjustment of the microscope known to man. With only one of them did I see anything but blackness or the familiar lacteal opacity, and that time I saw, to my pleasure and amazement, a variegated constellation of flecks, specks and dots. These I hastily drew. The instructor, noting my activity, came back from an adjoining desk, a smile on his lips and his eyebrows high in hope. He looked at my cell drawing. 'What's that?' he demanded, with a hint of a squeal in

He was beginning to quiver all over like Lionel Barrymore

his voice. 'That's what I saw,' I said. 'You didn't, you didn't, you *did*n't!' he screamed, losing control of his temper instantly, and he bent over and squinted into the microscope. His head snapped up. 'That's your eye!' he shouted. 'You've fixed the lens so that it reflects! You've drawn your eye!'

Another course that I didn't like, but somehow managed to pass, was economics. I went to that class straight from the botany class, which didn't help me any in understanding either subject. I used to get them mixed up. But not as mixed up as another student in my economics class who came there direct from a physics laboratory. He was a tackle on the football team, named Bolenciecwcz. At that time Ohio State University had one of the best football teams in the country, and Bolenciecwcz was one of its outstanding stars. In order to be eligible to play it was necessary for him to keep up in his studies, a very difficult matter, for while he was not dumber than an ox he was not any smarter. Most of his professors were lenient and helped him along. None gave him more hints, in answering questions, or asked him simpler ones than the economics professor, a thin, timid man named Bassum. One day when we were on the subject of transportation and distribution, it came Bolenciecwcz's turn to answer a question. 'Name one means of transportation,' the professor said to him. No light came into the big tackle's eyes. 'Just any means of transportation,' said the professor. Bolenciecwcz sat staring at him. 'That is,' pursued the professor, 'any medium, agency or method of going from one place to another.' Bolenciecwcz had the look of a man who is being led into a trap. 'You may choose among steam, horse-drawn or electrically propelled vehicles,' said the instructor. 'I might suggest the one which we commonly take in making long journeys across land.' There was a profound silence in which everybody stirred uneasily, including Bolenciecwcz and Mr Bassum. Mr Bassum abruptly broke this silence in an amazing manner. 'Choo-choo-choo,' he said, in a low voice, and turned instantly scarlet. He glanced appealingly around the room. All of us, of course, shared Mr Bassum's desire that Bolenciecwcz should stay abreast of the class in economics, for the Illinois game, one of the hardest and most important of the season, was only a week off. 'Toot, toot, too-toooooooot!' some student with a deep voice moaned, and we all looked encouragingly at Bolenciecwcz. Somebody else gave a fine imitation of a locomotive letting off steam. Mr Bassum himself rounded off the little show. 'Ding, dong, ding, dong,' he said hopefully. Bolenciecwcz was staring at the floor now, trying to think, his great brow furrowed, his huge hands rubbing together, his face red.

'How did you come to college this year, Mr Bolenciecwcz?' asked the professor. '*Chuff*a chuffa, *chuff*a chuffa.'

'M'father sent me,' said the football player.

'What on?' asked Bassum.

Bolenciecwcz was trying to think

'I git an 'lowance,' said the tackle, in a low, husky voice, obviously embarrassed.

'No, no,' said Bassum. 'Name a means of transportation. What did you *ride* here on?'

'Train,' said Bolenciecwcz.

'Quite right,' said the professor. 'Now, Mr Nugent, will you tell us—'

If I went through anguish in botany and economics – for different reasons – gymnasium work was even worse. I don't even like to think about it. They wouldn't let you play games or join in the exercises with your glasses on and I couldn't see with mine off. I bumped into professors, horizontal bars, agricultural students, and swinging iron rings. Not being able to see, I could take it but I couldn't dish it out. Also, in order to pass gymnasium (and you had to pass it to graduate) you had to learn to swim if you didn't know how. I didn't like the swimming pool, I didn't like swimming, and I didn't like the swimming instructor, and after all these years I still don't. I never swam but I passed my gym work anyway, by having another student give my gymnasium number (978) and swim across the pool in my place. He was a quiet, amiable blond youth, number 473, and he would have seen through a microscope for me if we could have got away with it, but we couldn't get away with it. Another thing I didn't like about gymnasium work was that they made you strip the day you registered. It is impossible for me to be happy when I am stripped and being asked a lot of questions. Still, I did better than a lanky agricultural student who was cross-examined just before I was. They asked each student what college he was in – that is, whether Arts, Engineering, Commerce, or Agriculture. 'What college are you in?' the instructor snapped at the youth in front of me. 'Ohio State University,' he said promptly.

It wasn't that agricultural student but it was another a whole lot like him who decided to take up journalism, possibly on the ground that when farming went to hell he could fall back on newspaper work. He didn't realise, of course, that that would be very much like falling back full-length on a kit of carpenter's tools. Haskins didn't seem cut out for journalism, being too embarrassed to talk to anybody and unable to use a typewriter, but the editor of the college paper assigned him to the cow barns, the sheep house, the horse pavilion, and the animal husbandry department generally. This was a genuinely big 'beat', for it took up five times as much ground and got ten times as great a legislative appropriation as the College of Liberal Arts. The agricultural student knew animals, but nevertheless his stories were dull and colourlessly written. He took all afternoon on each of them, on account of having to hunt for each letter on the typewriter. Once in a while he had to ask somebody to help him hunt. 'C' and 'L', in particular, were hard letters for him to find. His editor finally got pretty much annoyed at the farmer-journalist because his pieces were so uninteresting. 'See here, Haskins,' he snapped at him one day, 'why is it we never have anything hot from you on the horse pavilion? Here we have two hundred head of horses on this campus – more than any other university in the Western Conference except Purdue – and yet you never get any real low down on them. Now shoot over to the horse barns and dig up something lively.' Haskins shambled out and came back in about an hour; he said he had something. 'Well, start it off snappily,' said the editor. 'Something people will read.' Haskins set to work and in a couple of hours brought a sheet of typewritten paper to the desk; it was a two-hundred-word story about some disease that had broken out among the horses. Its opening sentence was simple but arresting. It read: 'Who has noticed the sores on the tops of the horses in the animal husbandry building?'

Ohio State was a land grant university and therefore two years of military drill was compulsory. We drilled with old Springfield rifles and studied the tactics of the Civil War even though the World War was going on at the time. At eleven o'clock each morning thousands of freshmen and sophomores used to deploy over the campus, moodily creeping up on the old chemistry building. It was good training for the kind of warfare that was waged at Shiloh but it had no connection with what was going on in Europe. Some people used to think there was German money behind it, but they didn't dare say so or they would have been thrown in jail as German spies. It was a period of muddy thought and marked, I believe, the decline of higher education in the Middle West.

As a soldier I was never any good at all. Most of the cadets were glumly indifferent soldiers, but I was no good at all. Once General Littlefield, who was commandant of the cadet corps, popped up in front of me during regimental drill and snapped, 'You are the main trouble with this university!' I think he meant that my type was the main trouble with the university but he may have meant me individually. I was mediocre at drill, certainly – that is, until my senior year. By that time I had drilled longer than anybody else in the Western Conference, having failed at military at the end of each preceding year so that I had to do it all over again. I was the only senior still in uniform. The uniform which, when new, had made me look like an inter-urban railway conductor, now that it had become faded and too tight made me look like Bert Williams in his bellboy act. This had a definitely bad effect on my morale. Even so, I had become by sheer practice little short of wonderful at squad manoeuvres.

One day General Littlefield picked our company out of the whole regiment and tried to get it mixed up by putting it through one movement after another as fast as we could execute them: squads right, squads left, squads on right into line, squads right about, squads left front into line etc. In about three minutes one hundred and nine men were marching in one direction and I was marching away from them at an angle of forty degrees, all alone. 'Company, halt!' shouted General Littlefield. 'That man is the only man who has it right!' I was made a corporal for my achievement.

The next day General Littlefield summoned me to his office. He was swatting flies when I went in. I was silent and he was silent too, for a long time. I don't think he remembered me or why he had sent for me, but he didn't want to admit it. He swatted some more flies, keeping his eyes on them narrowly before he let go with the swatter. 'Button up your coat!' he snapped. Looking back on it now I can see that he meant me although he was looking at a fly but I just stood there. Another fly came to rest on a paper in front of the general and began rubbing its hind legs together. The general lifted the swatter cautiously. I moved restlessly and the fly flew away. 'You startled him!' barked General Littlefield, looking at me severely. I said I was sorry. 'That won't help the situation!' snapped the General, with cold military logic. I didn't see what I could do except offer to chase some more flies toward his desk, but I didn't say anything. He stared out the window at the faraway figures of co-eds crossing the campus toward the library. Finally, he told me I could go. So I went. He either didn't know which cadet I was or else he forgot what he wanted to see me about. It may have been that he wished to apologise for having called me the main trouble with the university; or maybe he had decided to compliment me on my brilliant drilling of the day before and then at the last minute decided not to. I don't know. I don't think about it much any more.

Draft Board Nights

I left the University in June, 1918, but I couldn't get into the army on account of my sight, just as grandfather couldn't get in on account of his age. He applied several times and each time he took off his coat and threatened to whip the men who said he was too old. The disappointment of not getting to Germany (he saw no sense in everybody going to France) and the strain of running around town seeing influential officials finally got him down in bed. He had wanted to lead a division and his chagrin at not even being able to enlist as a private was too much for him. His brother Jake, some fifteen years younger than he was, sat up at night with him after he took to bed, because we were afraid he might leave the house without even putting on his clothes. Grandfather was against the idea of Jake watching over him – he thought it was a lot of tomfoolery – but Jake hadn't been able to sleep at night for twenty-eight years, so he was the perfect person for such a vigil.

On the third night, grandfather was wakeful. He would open his eyes, look at Jake, and close them again, frowning. He never answered any question Jake asked him. About four o'clock that morning, he caught his brother sound asleep in the big leather chair beside the bed. When once Jake did fall

About four o'clock he caught his brother asleep

asleep he slept deeply, so that grandfather was able to get up, dress himself, undress Jake, and put him in bed without waking him. When my Aunt Florence came into the room at seven o'clock, grandfather was sitting in the chair reading the *Memoirs of U.S. Grant* and Jake was sleeping in the bed. 'He watched while I slept,' said grandfather, 'so now I'm watchin' while he sleeps.' It seemed fair enough.

One reason we didn't want grandfather to roam around at

night was that he had said something once or twice about going over to Lancaster, his old home town, and putting his problem up to 'Cump' – that is, General William Tecumseh Sherman, also an old Lancaster boy. We knew that his inability to find Sherman would be bad for him and we were afraid that he might try to get there in the little electric runabout that had been bought for my grandmother. She had become, surprisingly enough, quite skilful at getting around town in it. Grandfather was astonished and a little indignant when he saw her get into the contraption and drive off smoothly and easily. It was her first vehicular triumph over him in almost fifty years of married life and he determined to learn to drive the thing himself. A famous old horseman, he approached it as he might have approached a wild colt. His brow would darken and he would begin to curse. He always leaped into it quickly, as if it might pull out from under him if he didn't get into the seat fast enough. The first few times he tried to run the electric, he went swiftly around in a small circle, drove over the kerb, across the sidewalk, and up, on to the lawn. We all tried to persuade him to give up, but his spirit was aroused. 'Git that goddam buggy back in the road!' he would say, imperiously. So we would manoeuvre it back into the street and he would try again. Pulling too savagely on the guiding-bar – to teach the electric a lesson – was what took him around in a circle, and it was difficult to make him understand that it was best to relax and not get mad. He had the notion that if you didn't hold her, she would throw you. And a man who (or so he often told us) had driven a four-horse McCormick reaper when he was five years old did not intend to be thrown by an electric runabout.

Since there was no way of getting him to give up learning to operate the electric, we would take him out to Franklin Park, where the roadways were wide and unfrequented, and spend an hour or so trying to explain the differences between driving a horse and carriage and driving an electric. He would keep muttering all the time; he never got it out of his head that when he took the driver's seat the machine flattened its ears on him, so to speak. After a few weeks, nevertheless, he got so he could run the electric for a hundred yards or so along a fairly straight line. But whenever he took a curve, he invariably pulled or pushed the bar too quickly and too hard and headed for a tree or a flower bed. Someone was always with him and we would never let him take the car out of the park.

One morning when grandmother was all ready to go to market, she called the garage and told them to send the electric around. They said that grandfather had already been there and taken it out. There was a tremendous to-do. We telephoned

There was a tremendous to-do

Uncle Will and he got out his Lozier and we started off to hunt for grandfather. It was not yet seven o'clock and there was fortunately little traffic. We headed for Franklin Park, figuring that he might have gone out there to try to break the car's spirit. One or two early pedestrians had seen a tall old gentleman with a white beard driving a little electric and cussing as he drove. We followed a tortuous trail and found them finally on Nelson Road, about four miles from the town of Shepard. Grandfather was standing in the road shouting, and the back wheels of the electric were deeply entangled in a barbed-wire fence. Two workmen and a farmhand were trying to get the thing loose. Grandfather was in a state of high wrath about the electric. 'The —— backed up on me!' he told us.

But to get back to the war. The Columbus draft board never called grandfather for service, which was a lucky thing for them because they would have had to take him. There were stories that several old men of eighty or ninety had been summoned in the confusion, but somehow or other grandfather was missed. He waited every day for the call, but it never came. My own experience was quite different. I was called almost every week, even though I had been exempted from service the first time I went before the medical examiners. Either they were never convinced that it was me or else there was some clerical error in the records which was never cleared up. Anyway, there was usually a letter for me on Monday ordering me to report for examination on the second floor of Memorial Hall the following Wednesday at 9 p.m. The second time I went up I tried to explain to one of the doctors that I had already been exempted. 'You're just a blur to me,' I said, taking off my glasses. 'You're absolutely nothing to me,' he snapped, sharply.

I had to take off all my clothes each time and jog around the hall with a lot of porters and bank presidents' sons and clerks and poets. Our hearts and lungs would be examined, and then our feet; and finally our eyes. That always came last. When the eye specialist got around to me, he would always say, 'Why, you couldn't get into the service with sight like that!' 'I know,' I would say. Then a week or two later I would be summoned again and go through the same rigmarole. The ninth or tenth time I was called, I happened to pick up one of several stethoscopes that were lying on a table and suddenly, instead of finding myself in the line of draft men, I found myself in the line of examiners. 'Hallo, Doctor,' said one of them, nodding. 'Hallo,' I said. That, of course, was before I took my clothes off. I might have managed it naked, but I doubt it. I was assigned, or rather drifted, to the chest-and-lung section, where I began to examine every other man, thus cutting old Dr Ridgeway's work in two. 'I'm glad to have you here, Doctor,' he said.

I passed most of the men that came to me, but now and then I would exempt one just to be on the safe side. I began by making each of them hold his breath and then say 'mi, mi, mi, mi', until I noticed Ridgeway looking at me curiously. He, I discovered, simply made them say 'ah', and sometimes he didn't make them say anything. Once I got hold of a man who, it came out

An abdominal man worrying

later, had swallowed a watch – to make the doctors believe
there was something wrong with him inside (it was a common
subterfuge: men swallowed nails, hairpins, ink, etc., in an
effort to be let out). Since I didn't know what you were supposed to hear through a stethoscope, the ticking of the watch
at first didn't surprise me, but I decided to call Dr Ridgeway
into consultation, because nobody else had ticked. 'This man
seems to tick,' I said to him. He looked at me in surprise but
didn't say anything. Then he thumped the man, laid his ear to
his chest, and finally tried the stethoscope. 'Sound as a dollar,'
he said. 'Listen lower down,' I told him. The man indicated his
stomach. Ridgeway gave him a haughty, indignant look. 'That
is for the abdominal men to worry about,' he said, and moved

off. A few minutes later, Dr Blythe Ballomy got around to the man and listened, but he didn't blink an eye; his grim expression never changed. 'You have swallowed a watch, my man,' he said, crisply. The draftee reddened in embarrassment and uncertainty. 'On *purpose*?' he asked. 'That I can't say,' the doctor told him, and went on.

I served with the draft board for about four months. Until the summonses ceased, I couldn't leave town and as long as I stayed and appeared promptly for examination, even though I did the examining, I felt that technically I could not be convicted of evasion. During the daytime, I worked as publicity agent for an amusement park, the manager of which was a tall, unexpected young man named Byron Landis. Some years before, he had dynamited the men's lounge in the statehouse annexe for a prank: he enjoyed pouring buckets of water on sleeping persons, and once he had barely escaped arrest for jumping off the top of the old Columbus Transfer Company building with a homemade parachute.

He asked me one morning if I would like to take a ride in the new Scarlet Tornado, a steep and wavy roller-coaster. I didn't want to but I was afraid he would think I was afraid, so I went along. It was about ten o'clock and there was nobody at the park except workmen and attendants and concessionaires in their shirt-sleeves. We climbed into one of the long gondolas of the roller-coaster and while I was looking around for the man who was going to run it, we began to move off. Landis, I discovered, was running it himself. But it was too late to get out; we had begun to climb, clickety-clockety, up the first steep incline, down the other side of which we careened at eighty miles an hour. 'I didn't know you could run this thing!' I bawled at my companion, as we catapulted up a sixty-degree arch and looped headlong into space. 'I didn't either!' he bawled back. The racket and the rush of air were terrific as we roared into the pitch-black Cave of Darkness and came out and down Monohan's Leap, so called because a workman named Monohan had been forced to jump from it when caught between two approaching experimental cars while it was being completed. That trip, although it ended safely, made a lasting impression on me. It is not too much to say that it has flavoured my life. It is the reason I shout in my sleep, refuse to ride on the elevator, keep jerking the emergency brake in cars other people are driving, have the sensation of flying like a bird when I first lie down, and in certain months can't keep anything in my stomach.

During my last few trips to the draft board, I went again as a draft prospect, having grown tired of being an examiner. None of the doctors who had been my colleagues for so long recognised me, not even Dr Ridgeway. When he examined my chest for the last time, I asked him if there hadn't been another doctor helping him. He said there had been. 'Did he look anything like me?' I asked. Dr Ridgeway looked at me. 'I don't think so,' he said, 'he was taller.' (I had my shoes off while he was examining me.) 'A good pulmonary man,' added Ridgeway. 'Relative of yours?' I said yes. He sent me on to Dr Quimby, the specialist who had examined my eyes twelve or fifteen times before. He gave me some simple reading tests. 'You could never get into the army with eyes like that,' he said. 'I know,' I told him.

Late one morning, shortly after my last examination, I was awakened by the sound of bells ringing and whistles blowing. It grew louder and more insistent and wilder. It was the Armistice.

A Note at the End

The hard times of my middle years I pass over, leaving the ringing bells of 1918, with all their false promise, to mark the end of a special sequence. The sharp edges of old reticences are softened in the autobiographer by the passing of time – a man does not pull the pillow over his head when he wakes in the morning because he suddenly remembers some awful thing that happened to him fifteen or twenty years ago, but the confusions and the panics of last year and the year before are too close for contentment. Until a man can quit talking loudly to himself in order to shout down the memories of blunderings and gropings, he is in no shape for the painstaking examination of distress and the careful ordering of events so necessary to a calm and balanced exposition of what, exactly, was the matter. The time I fell out of the gun-room in Mr James Stanley's house in Green Lake, New York, is, for instance, much too near for me to go into with any peace of mind, although it happened in 1925, the ill-fated year of 'Horses, Horses, Horses' and 'Valencia'. There is now, I understand, a porch to walk out on to when you open the door I opened that night, but there wasn't then.

The mistaken exits and entrances of my thirties have moved me several times to some thought of spending the rest of my days wandering aimlessly around the South Seas, like a character out of Conrad, silent and inscrutable. But the necessity for frequent visits to my oculist and dentist has prevented this. You can't be running back from Singapore every few months to get your lenses changed and still retain the proper mood for wandering. Furthermore, my horn-rimmed glasses and my Ohio accent betray me, even when I sit on the terraces of little tropical cafés, wearing a pith helmet, staring straight ahead, and twitching a muscle in my jaw. I found this out when I tried wandering around the West Indies one summer. Instead of being followed by the whispers of men and the glances of women, I was followed by bead salesmen and native women with postcards. Nor did any dark girl, looking at all like Tondelaya in *White Cargo*, come forward and offer to go to pieces with me. They tried to sell me baskets.

Under these circumstances it is impossible to be inscrutable and a wanderer who isn't inscrutable might just as well be back at Broad and High Streets in Columbus sitting in the Baltimore

They tried to sell me baskets

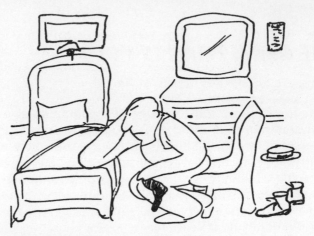

A hotel room in Louisville

Dairy Lunch. Nobody from Columbus has ever made a first rate wanderer in the Conradean tradition. Some of them have been fairly good at disappearing for a few days to turn up in a hotel in Louisville with a bad headache and no recollection of how they got there, but they always scurry back to their wives with some cock-and-bull story of having lost their memory or having gone away to attend the annual convention of the Fraternal Order of Eagles.

There was, of course, even for Conrad's Lord Jim, no running away. The cloud of his special discomfiture followed him like a pup, no matter what ships he took or what wildernesses he entered. In the pathways between office and home and home and houses of settled people there are always, ready to snap at you, the little perils of routine living, but there is no escape in the unplanned tangent, the sudden turn. In Martinique, when the whistle blew for the tourists to get back on the ship, I had a quick, wild, and lovely moment when I decided I wouldn't get back on the ship. I did, though. And I found that somebody had stolen the pants to my dinner jacket.

THE GENTLEMAN IS COLD

In the first chill days of November it was the subject of sharp and rather nasty comment on the part of my friends and colleagues that I went about the draughty streets of town without a hat or overcoat. Once even a stranger who passed me in the street snarled, 'Put on your hat and coat!' It seemed to annoy people. They began to insinuate under their breath, and even come right out and say, that I was simply trying to look strange and different in order to attract attention. This accusation was made with increasing bitterness when my hair, which I always forget to have cut, began to get very long. It was obvious, my friends said, that I walked about the city cold and miserable in the hope that people would nudge their companions and say, 'There goes Jacob Thurman, the eccentric essayist.'

There was, and is, no basis to these charges at all. I have reasons, and good reasons, for not wanting to, for, in fact, not being able to, wear an overcoat. I have just as good reasons about the hat, but I needn't go into them so fully. A week or so ago, however, the smirking remarks and mean innuendoes of my associates forced me one day to put on my overcoat (I couldn't find my hat and I wouldn't buy a new one, because when I try one on and peer in the triplicate mirrors they have in hat shops, I catch unexpected angles of my face which make me look like a slightly ill professor of botany who is also lost). The overcoat, which I bought in 1930, after a brief and losing battle with a sharp-tongued clerk who was taller than I am, does not fit me very well and never did fit me very well. That's one reason I don't like to wear it. Another is that it has no buttons (it didn't have any buttons after the first week) and is extremely difficult to manage in a head wind. In such a wind I used to grab for my hat with both hands, thus letting go the hold I had on my coat to keep it together in front, and the whole thing would belly out all around me. Once, in grabbing for my hat (and missing it, for I was a fraction of a second too late), I knocked my glasses off and was not only caught in a grotesque swirl of overcoat right at the corner of Fifth Avenue and Forty-fourth Street but couldn't see a thing. Several people stopped and watched the struggle without offering to help until finally, when everybody had had his laugh, a woman picked up my glasses and handed them to me. 'Here's your glasses,' she tittered, grinning at me as if I were a policeman's horse with a sunbonnet. I put the glasses on, gathered the coat together, and walked off with as much dignity as I could, leaving my hat swirling along the street under the wheels of traffic.

It was the twentieth of November this winter that I finally put on my overcoat for the first time. It is a heavy grey one, and looks a little like a dog bed because the strap on the inside of the collar broke and the coat had been lying on the floor of my closet for almost a year. I carried it downstairs from my hotel room to the lobby, and didn't start to put it on until I had reached the revolving doors leading to the street. I had just got one arm into a sleeve when I was suddenly grabbed from behind, a hand shot up under the coat, jerked my undercoat sharply down, and I fell backward, choking, into the arms of the hotel doorman, who had come to my assistance. He is a powerfully built man who brooks no denial of, or interference with, his little attentions and services. He didn't exactly throw me, but I took a pretty bad tossing around.

From the hotel I went, in a badly disturbed state of mind, to my barber's, and I was just reaching into a pocket of the overcoat for my cigarettes and matches when the coat was whisked off me from behind. This was done with great firmness but no skill by the coloured porter and bootblack who sneaks up behind people at Joe's barbershop and tears their overcoats off their backs. This porter is not so powerfully built as the doorman at my hotel, but he is sinewy and in excellent condition. Furthermore, he was not wearing an overcoat himself, and the man who is wearing an overcoat is at a great disadvantage in a struggle. This porter is also a coat-tugger, belonging to that school of coat-tuggers who reach up under your overcoat after they have helped you on with it and jerk the back of your suit jacket so savagely that the collar of the jacket is pulled away from its proper set around the shoulders and makes you feel loutish and miserable. There is nothing to do about this except give the man a dime.

88

It wasn't, however, until I went with some fine acquaintances of mine to an excellent restaurant that night that I got into my old familiar plight with the ripped lining of the left sleeve. After dining, the gentlemen in the party were helped on with their coats by one of those slim, silent waiters with the cold and fishy eye of an art critic. He got me adroitly into the right sleeve of my overcoat, and then I stuck my left arm smoothly into the lining of the other sleeve. Running an arm into the ripped lining of an overcoat while people, both acquaintances and strangers, look on and the eye of the struggling waiter gets colder and colder, is one of the most humiliating experiences known to the American male. After it was finally straightened out and I got my arm through the sleeve, I couldn't find any money for a tip; I couldn't even find a dime. I don't like to dwell on that incident.

After leaving the restaurant, we went to a theatre, and there another reason I do not like to wear an overcoat and never will wear an overcoat again reared its terrifying head. In taking off my overcoat to hand it to the unsympathetic hat-check boy, I took off with it the jacket to my dinner clothes and was left standing in the crowded and well-dressed lounge in my shirt-sleeves, with a section of my suspenders plainly visible through the armhole of my waistcoat. So speedily do hat-check boys work that my overcoat and jacket had been whisked to the back of the hat-check room and hung up under a couple of other overcoats before I could do anything about it. The eight or ten seconds that went by before I recovered my dinner jacket were among the worst moments of my life. The only worse experience I can think of was the time my suitcase flopped open on the Madison Avenue car tracks when I was hurrying to make a train at Grand Central.

I tried to pass off the episode of the dinner jacket nonchalantly, but succeeded only in lapsing into that red-faced fixed grin which no truly well-poised man-about-town ever permits himself to lapse into. I reached for my cigarettes, but I found that I had left them in a pocket of my overcoat, so in order to have something to do with my hands – for people were still staring and leering – I gracefully pulled a neatly folded handkerchief from the breast pocket of my dinner jacket, only to discover when I shook it out that it was a clean white silk sock. The last time I had dressed for dinner, I had been unable to find a fresh handkerchief, and after considerable effort had finally folded the sock and tucked it into the pocket of my jacket in such a way that it looked like a handkerchief. Of course, on that occasion I had remembered not to pull the handkerchief out. I had remembered this by grimly repeating it to myself all evening, but that had been several nights before and I had completely forgotten about the sock.

I would never have brought out all these humiliating revelations had it not been for the fact that even those persons who know me best, for a modest, unassuming man, had really come to believe that I went around town without an overcoat in order to make the same kind of impression that Oscar Wilde made with his sunflower or Sean O'Casey with his brown sweater. I simply want to be mentally at ease, and I have found out after years of experience that I cannot be mentally at ease and at the same time wear an overcoat. Going without an overcoat in bitter weather has, God knows, its special humiliations, but having a kindly old lady come up to me on the street and hand me a dime is nothing compared to the horrors I went through when I wore an overcoat, or tried to wear one.

THE DEPARTURE OF EMMA INCH

Emma Inch looked no different from any other middle-aged, thin woman you might glance at in the subway or deal with across the counter of some small store in a country town, and then forget forever. Her hair was drab and unabundant, her face made no impression on you, her voice I don't remember – it was just a voice. She came to us with a letter of recommendation from some acquaintance who knew that we were going to Martha's Vineyard for the summer and wanted a cook. We took her because there was nobody else, and she seemed all right. She had arrived at our hotel in Forty-fifth Street the day before we were going to leave and we got her a room for the night, because she lived way uptown somewhere. She said she really ought to go back and give up her room, but I told her I'd fix that.

Emma Inch had a big scuffed brown suitcase with her, and a Boston bull terrier. His name was Feely. Feely was seventeen years old and he grumbled and growled and snuffled all the time, but we needed a cook and we agreed to take Feely along with Emma Inch, if she would take care of him and keep him out of the way. It turned out to be easy to keep Feely out of the way because he would lie grousing anywhere Emma put him until she came and picked him up again. I never saw him walk. Emma had owned him, she said, since he was a pup. He was

all she had in the world, she told us, with a mist in her eyes. I felt embarrassed but not touched. I didn't see how anybody could love Feely.

I didn't lose any sleep about Emma Inch and Feely the night of the day they arrived, but my wife did. She told me next morning that she had lain awake a long time thinking about the cook and her dog, because she felt kind of funny about them. She didn't know why. She just had a feeling that they were kind of funny. When we were all ready to leave – it was about three o'clock in the afternoon, for we had kept putting off the packing – I phoned Emma's room, but she didn't answer. It was getting late and we felt nervous – the Fall River boat would sail in about two hours. We couldn't understand why we hadn't heard anything from Emma and Feely. It wasn't until four o'clock that we did. There was a small rap on the door of our bedroom and I opened it and Emma and Feely were there, Feely in her arms, snuffing and snaffling, as if he had been swimming a long way.

My wife told Emma to get her bag packed, we were leaving in a little while. Emma said her bag *was* packed, except for her electric fan, and she couldn't get that in. 'You won't need an electric fan at the Vineyard,' my wife told her. 'It's cool there, even during the day, and it's almost cold at night. Besides, there is no electricity in the cottage we are going to.' Emma Inch seemed distressed. She studied my wife's face. 'I'll have to think of something else then,' she said. 'Mebbe I could let the water run all night.' We both sat down and looked at her. Feely's asthmatic noises were the only sounds in the room for a while. 'Doesn't that dog ever stop that?' I asked, irritably. 'Oh, he's just talking,' said Emma. 'He talks all the time, but I'll keep him in my room and he won't bother you none.' 'Doesn't he bother you?' I asked. 'He *would* bother me', said Emma, 'at night, but I put the electric fan on and keep the light burning. He don't make so much noise when it's light, because he don't snore. The fan kind of keeps me from noticing him. I put a piece of cardboard, like, where the fan hits it and then I don't notice Feely so much. Mebbe I could let the water run in my room all night instead of the fan.' I said 'Hmmm' and got up and mixed a drink for my wife and me – we had decided not to have one till we got on the boat, but I thought we'd better have one now. My wife didn't tell Emma there would be no running water in her room at the Vineyard.

'We've been worried about you, Emma,' I said. 'I phoned your room but you didn't answer.' 'I never answer the phone,' said Emma, 'because I always get a shock. I wasn't there anyways. I couldn't sleep in that room. I went back to Mrs McCoy's on Seventy-eighth Street.' I lowered my glass. 'You went back to Seventy-eighth Street last *night*?' I demanded. 'Yes, sir,' she said. 'I had to tell Mrs McCoy I was going away and wouldn't be there any more for a while – Mrs McCoy's the landlady. Anyways, I never sleep in a hotel.' She looked around the room. 'They burn down,' she told us.

It came out that Emma Inch had not only gone back to Seventy-eighth Street the night before but had walked all the way, carrying Feely. It had taken her an hour or two, because Feely didn't like to be carried very far at a time, so she had had to stop every block or so and put him down on the side-walk for a while. It had taken her just as long to walk back to our hotel, too; Feely, it seems, never got up before afternoon – that's why she was so late. She was sorry. My wife and I finished our drinks, looking at each other, and at Feely.

Emma Inch didn't like the idea of riding to Pier 14 in a taxi, but after ten minutes of cajoling and pleading she finally got in. 'Make it go slow,' she said. We had enough time, so I asked the driver to take it easy. Emma kept getting to her feet and I kept pulling her back onto the seat. 'I never been in an automobile before,' she said. 'It goes awful fast.' Now and then she gave a little squeal of fright. The driver turned his head and grinned. 'You're O.K. wit' me, lady,' he said. Feely growled at him. Emma waited until he had turned away again, and then she leaned over to my wife and whispered. 'They all take cocaine,' she said. Feely began to make a new sound – a kind of high, agonised yelp. 'He's singing,' said Emma. She gave a strange little giggle, but the expression of her face didn't change. 'I wish you had put the Scotch where we could get at it,' said my wife.

If Emma Inch had been afraid of the taxi-cab, she was terrified by the *Priscilla* of the Fall River Line. 'I don't think I can go,' said Emma. 'I don't think I could get on a boat. I didn't know they were so big.' She stood rooted to the pier, clasping Feely. She must have squeezed him too hard, for he screamed –

93

he screamed like a woman. We all jumped. 'It's his ears,' said Emma. 'His ears hurt.' We finally got her on the boat, and once aboard, in the salon, her terror abated somewhat. Then the three parting blasts of the boat whistle rocked lower Manhattan. Emma Inch leaped to her feet and began to run, letting go of her suitcase (which she had refused to give up to a porter) but holding onto Feely. I caught her just as she reached the gangplank. The ship was on its way when I let go of her arm.

It was a long time before I could get Emma to go to her stateroom, but she went at last. It was an inside stateroom, and she didn't seem to mind it. I think she was surprised to find that it was like a room, and had a bed and a chair and washbowl. She put Feely down on the floor. 'I think you'll have to do something about the dog,' I said. 'I think they put them somewhere and you get them when you get off.' 'No, they don't,' said Emma. I guess, in this case, they didn't. I don't know. I shut the door on Emma Inch and Feely, and went away. My wife was drinking straight Scotch when I got to our stateroom.

The next morning, cold and early, we got Emma and Feely off the *Priscilla* at Fall River and over to New Bedford in a taxi and onto the little boat for Martha's Vineyard. Each move was as difficult as getting a combative drunken man out of the night club in which he fancies he has been insulted. Emma sat in a chair on the Vineyard boat, as far away from sight of the water as she could get, and closed her eyes and held onto Feely. She had thrown a coat over Feely, not only to keep him warm but to prevent any of the ship's officers from taking him away from her. I went in from the deck at intervals to see how she was. She was all right, or at least all right for her, until five minutes before the boat reached the dock at Woods Hole, the only stop between New Bedford and the Vineyard. Then Feely got sick. Or at any rate Emma said he was sick. He didn't seem to me any different from what he always was – his breathing was just as abnormal and irregular. But Emma said he was sick. There were tears in her eyes. 'He's a very sick dog, Mr Thurman,' she said. 'I'll have to take him home.' I knew by the way she said 'home' what she meant. She meant Seventy-eighth Street.

The boat tied up at Woods Hole and was motionless and we could hear the racket of the deckhands on the dock loading freight. 'I'll get off here,' said Emma, firmly, or with more firmness, anyway, than she had shown yet. I explained to her that we would be home in half an hour, that everything would be fine then, everything would be wonderful. I said Feely would be a new dog. I told her people sent sick dogs to Martha's Vineyard to be cured. But it was no good. 'I'll have to take him off here,' said Emma. 'I always have to take him home when he is sick.' I talked to her eloquently about the loveliness of Martha's Vineyard and the nice houses and the nice people and the wonderful accommodations for dogs. But I knew it was useless. I could tell by looking at her. She was going to get off the boat at Woods Hole.

'You really can't do this,' I said, grimly, shaking her arm. Feely snarled weakly. 'You haven't any money and you don't know where you are. You're a long way from New York. Nobody ever got from Woods Hole to New York alone.' She didn't seem to hear me. She began walking toward the stairs leading to the gangplank, crooning to Feely. 'You'll have to go all the way back on boats,' I said, 'or else take a train, and you haven't any money. If you are going to be so stupid and leave us now, I can't give you any money.' 'I don't want any money, Mr Thurman,' she said. 'I haven't earned any money.' I walked along in irritable silence for a moment; then I gave her some money. I made her take it. We got to the gangplank. Feely snaffled and gurgled. I saw now that his eyes were a little red and moist. I knew it would do no good to summon my wife – not when Feely's health was at stake. 'How do you expect to get home from here?' I almost shouted at Emma Inch as she moved down the gangplank. 'You're way out on the end of Massachusetts.' She stopped and turned around. 'We'll walk,' she said. 'We like to walk, Feely and me.' I just stood still and watched her go.

When I went up on deck, the boat was clearing for the Vineyard. 'How's everything?' asked my wife. I waved a hand in the direction of the dock. Emma Inch was standing there, her suitcase at her feet, her dog under one arm, waving goodbye to us with her free hand. I had never seen her smile before, but she was smiling now.

THERE'S AN OWL IN MY ROOM

I saw Gertrude Stein on the screen of a newsreel theatre one afternoon and I heard her read that famous passage of hers about pigeons on the grass, alas (the sorrow is, as you know, Miss Stein's). After reading about the pigeons on the grass alas, Miss Stein said, 'This is a simple description of a landscape I have seen many times.' I don't really believe that that is true. Pigeons on the grass alas may be a simple description of Miss Stein's own consciousness, but it is not a simple description of a plot of grass on which pigeons have alighted, are alighting, or are going to alight. A truly simple description of the pigeons alighting on the grass of the Luxembourg Gardens (which, I believe, is where the pigeons alighted) would say of the pigeons alighting there only that they were pigeons alighting. Pigeons that alight anywhere are neither sad pigeons nor gay pigeons, they are simply pigeons.

It is neither just nor accurate to connect the word alas with pigeons. Pigeons are definitely not alas. They have nothing to do with alas and they have nothing to do with hooray (not even when you tie red, white, and blue ribbons on them and let them loose at band concerts); they have nothing to do with mercy me or isn't that fine, either. White rabbits, yes, and Scotch terriers, and bluejays, and even hippopotamuses, but not pigeons. I happen to have studied pigeons very closely and carefully, and I have studied the effect, or rather the lack of effect, of pigeons very carefully. A number of pigeons alight from time to time on the sill of my hotel window when I am eating breakfast and staring out the window. They never alas me, they never make me feel alas; they never make me feel anything.

Nobody and no animal and no other bird can play a scene so far down as a pigeon can. For instance, when a pigeon on my window ledge becomes aware of me sitting there in a chair in my blue polka-dot dressing-gown, worrying, he pokes his head far out from his shoulders and peers sideways at me, for all the world (Miss Stein might surmise) like a timid man peering around the corner of a building trying to ascertain whether he is being followed by some hoofed fiend or only by the echo of his own footsteps. And yet it is *not* for all the world like a timid man peering around the corner of a building trying to ascertain whether he is being followed by a hoofed fiend or only by the echo of his own footsteps, at all. And that is because there is no emotion in the pigeon and no power to arouse emotion. A pigeon looking is just a pigeon looking. When it comes to emotion, a fish, compared to a pigeon, is practically beside himself.

A pigeon peering at me doesn't make me sad or glad or apprehensive or hopeful. With a horse or a cow or a dog it would be different. It would be especially different with a dog. Some dogs peer at me as if I had just gone completely crazy or as if they had just gone completely crazy. I can go so far as to say that most dogs peer at me that way. This creates in the consciousness of both me and the dog a feeling of alarm or downright terror and legitimately permits me to work into a description of the landscape, in which the dog and myself are

figures, a note of emotion. Thus I should not have minded if Miss Stein had written: dogs on the grass, look out, dogs on the grass, look out, look out, dogs on the grass, look out Alice. That would be a simple description of dogs on the grass. But when any writer pretends that a pigeon makes him sad, or makes him anything else, I must instantly protest that this is a highly specialised fantastic impression created in an individual consciousness and that therefore it cannot fairly be presented as a simple description of what actually was to be seen.

People who do not understand pigeons – and pigeons can be understood only when you understand that there is nothing to understand about them – should not go around describing pigeons or the effect of pigeons. Pigeons come closer to a zero of impingement than any other birds. Hens embarrass me the way my old Aunt Hattie used to when I was twelve and she still insisted I wasn't big enough to bathe myself; owls disturb me; if I am with an eagle I always pretend that I am not with an eagle; and so on down to swallows at twilight who scare the hell out of me. But pigeons have absolutely no effect on me. They have absolutely no effect on anybody. They couldn't even startle a child. That is why they are selected from among all birds to be let loose, with coloured ribbons attached to them, at band concerts, library dedications, and christenings of new dirigibles. If anybody let loose a lot of owls on such an occasion there would be rioting and catcalls and whistling and fainting spells and throwing of chairs and the Lord only knows what else.

From where I am sitting now I can look out the window and see a pigeon being a pigeon on the roof of the Harvard Club. No other thing can be less what it is not than a pigeon can, and Miss Stein, of all people, should understand that simple fact. Behind the pigeon I am looking at, a blank wall of tired grey bricks is stolidly trying to sleep off oblivion; underneath the pigeon the cloistered windows of the Harvard Club are staring in horrified bewilderment at something they have seen across the street. The pigeon is just there on the roof being a pigeon, having been, and being, a pigeon and, what is more, always going to be, too. Nothing could be simpler than that. If you read that sentence aloud you will instantly see what I mean. It is a simple description of a pigeon on a roof. It is only with an effort that I am conscious of the pigeon, but I am acutely aware of a great sulky red iron pipe that is creeping up the side of the building intent on sneaking up on a slightly tipsy chimney which is shouting its head off.

There is nothing a pigeon can do or be that would make me feel sorry for it or for myself or for the people in the world, just as there is nothing I could do or be that would make a pigeon feel sorry for itself. Even if I plucked his feathers out it would not make him feel sorry for himself and it would not make me feel sorry for myself or for him. But try plucking the quills out of a porcupine or even plucking the fur out of a jackrabbit. There is nothing a pigeon could be, or can be, rather, which could get into my consciousness like a fumbling hand in a bureau drawer and disarrange my mind or pull anything out of it. I bar nothing at all. You could dress up a pigeon in a tiny suit of evening clothes and put a tiny silk hat on his head and a tiny gold-headed cane under his wing and send him walking into my room at night. It would make no impression on me. I would not shout, 'Good god amighty, the birds are in charge!' But you could send an owl into my room, dressed only in the feathers it was born with, and no monkey business, and I would pull the covers over my head and scream.

No other thing in the world falls so far short of being able to do what it cannot do as a pigeon does. Of being *unable* to do what it *can* do, too, as far as that goes.

A PORTRAIT OF AUNT IDA

My mother's Aunt Ida Clemmens died the other day out West. She was ninety-one years old. I remember her clearly, although I haven't thought about her in a long time and never saw her after I was twenty. I remember how dearly she loved catastrophes, especially those of a national or international importance. The sinking of the *Titanic* was perhaps the most important tragedy of the years in which I knew her. She never saw in such things, as her older sisters, Emma and Clara, did, the vengeance of a Deity outraged by Man's lust for speed and gaiety; she looked for the causes deep down in the dark heart of the corporate interests. You could never make her believe that the *Titanic* hit an iceberg. Whoever *heard* of such a thing! It was simply a flimsy prevarication devised to cover up the real cause. The real cause she could not, or would not, make plain, but somewhere in its black core was a monstrous secret of treachery and corrupt goings-on – men were like that. She came later on to doubt the courage of the brave gentlemen on the sinking ship who at the last waved goodbye smilingly and smoked cigarettes. It was her growing conviction that most of them had to be shot by the ship's officers in order to prevent them from crowding into the lifeboats ahead of the older and less attractive women passengers. Eminence and wealth in men Aunt Ida persistently attributed to deceit, trickery, and impiety. I think the only famous person she ever trusted in her time was President McKinley.

The disappearance of Judge Crater, the Hall-Mills murder, the Starr Faithfull case, and similar mysteries must have made Aunt Ida's last years happy. She loved the unsolvable and the unsolved. Mysteries that were never cleared up were brought about, in her opinion, by the workings of some strange force in the world which we do not thoroughly understand and which God does not intend that we ever shall understand. An invisible power, a power akin to electricity and radio (both of which she must have regarded as somehow or other blasphemous), but never to be isolated or channelled. Out of this power came murder, disappearances, and supernatural phenomena. All persons connected in any way whatever with celebrated cases were tainted in Aunt Ida's sight – and that went for prosecuting attorneys, too (always 'tricky' men). But she would, I'm sure, rather have had a look at Willie Stevens than at President Roosevelt, at Jafsie than at the King of England, just as she would rather have gone through the old Wendel house than the White House.

Surgical operations and post-mortems were among Aunt Ida's special interests, although she did not believe that any operation was ever necessary and she was convinced that post-mortems were conducted to cover up something rather than to find something out. It was her conviction that doctors were in the habit of trying to obfuscate or distort the true facts about illness and death. She believed that many of her friends and relatives had been laid away without the real causes of their deaths being entered on the 'city books'. She was fond of telling a long and involved story about the death of one of her first cousins, a married woman who had passed away at twenty-five. Aunt Ida for thirty years contended that there was something 'behind it'. She believed that a certain physician, a gentleman of the highest reputation, would some day 'tell the truth about Ruth', perhaps on his deathbed. When he died (without confessing, of course), she said after reading the account in the newspaper that she had dreamed of him a few nights before. It seemed that he had called to her and wanted to tell her something but couldn't.

Aunt Ida believed that she was terribly psychic. She had warnings, premonitions, and 'feelings'. They were invariably intimations of approaching misfortune, sickness, or death. She never had a premonition that everything was going to be all right. It was always that Grace So-and-So was not going to marry the man she was engaged to, or that Mr Hollowell, who was down in South America on business, would never return, or that old Mrs Hutchins would not last out the year (she missed on old Mrs Hutchins for twenty-two years but finally made it). Most all of Aunt Ida's forewarnings of financial ruin and marital tragedy came in the daytime while she was marketing or sitting hulling peas; most all of her intimations of death appeared to her in dreams. Dreams of Ohio women of Aunt Ida's generation were never Freudian; they were purely prophetic. They dealt with black hearses and white hearses rolling soundlessly along through the night, and with coffins being carried out of houses, and with tombstones bearing names and dates, and with tall, faceless women in black veils and gloves. Most of Aunt Ida's dreams foretold the fate of women, for what happened to women was of much greater importance to Aunt Ida than what happened to men. Men usually 'brought things on themselves'; women, on the other hand, were usually the victims of dark and devious goings-on of a more or less supernatural nature.

Birth was, in some ways, as dark a matter to Aunt Ida as death. She felt that most babies, no matter what you said or anybody else said, were 'not wanted'. She believed that the children of famous people, brilliant people, and of first, second, or third cousins would be idiotic. If a child died young, she laid it to the child's parentage, no matter what the immediate cause of death might have been. 'There is something in that family,' Aunt Ida used to say, in her best funeral voice. This something was a vague, ominous thing, both far off and close at hand, misty and ready to spring, compounded of nobody could guess exactly what. One of Aunt Ida's favourite predictions was 'They'll never raise that baby, you mark my words.' The fact that they usually did never shook her confidence in her 'feeling'. If she was right once in twenty times, it proved that she knew what she was talking about. In foretelling the sex of unborn children, she was right about half the time.

Life after death was a source of speculation, worry, and exhilaration to Aunt Ida. She firmly believed that people could 'come back' and she could tell you of many a house that was haunted (barrels of apples rolled down the attic steps of one of them, I remember, but it was never clear why they did). Aunt Ida put no faith in mediums or séances. The dead preferred to come back to the houses where they had lived and to go stalking through the rooms and down the halls. I think Aunt Ida always thought of them as coming back in the flesh, fully clothed, for she always spoke of them as 'the dead', never as ghosts. The reason they came back was that they had left something unsaid or undone that must be corrected. Although a descendant of staunch orthodox Methodists, some of them ministers, Aunt Ida in her later years dabbled a little in various religions, superstitions, and even cults. She found astrology, New Thought, and the theory of reincarnation comforting. The people who are bowed down in this life, she grew to believe, will have another chance.

Aunt Ida was confident that the world was going to be destroyed almost any day. When Halley's comet appeared in 1910, she expected to read in the papers every time she picked them up the news that Paris had gone up in flames and that New York City had slid into the ocean. Those two cities, being horrible dens of vice, were bound to go first; the smaller towns would be destroyed in a more leisurely fashion with some respectable and dignified ending for the pious and the kindly people.

Two of Aunt Ida's favourite expressions were 'I never heard of such a thing' and 'If I never get up from this chair . . .' She told all stories of death, misfortune, grief, corruption, and disaster with vehemence and exaggeration. She was hampered in narration by her inability to think of names, particularly simple names, such as Joe, Earl, Ned, Harry, Louise, Ruth, Bert. Somebody usually had to prompt her with the name of the third cousin, or whomever, that she was trying to think of, but she was unerring in her ability to remember difficult names the rest of us had long forgotten. 'He used to work in the old Schirtzberger & Wallenheim saddle store in Naughton Street,' she would say. 'What *was* his name?' It would turn out that his name was Frank Butler.

Up to the end, they tell me, Aunt Ida could read without her glasses, and none of the commoner frailties of senility affected her. She had no persecution complex, no lapses of memory, no trailing off into the past, no unfounded bitternesses – unless you could call her violent hatred of cigarettes unfounded bitterness, and I don't think it was, because she actually knew stories of young men and even young women who had become paralysed to the point of losing the use of both legs through smoking cigarettes. She tended to her begonias and wrote out a cheque for the rent the day she took to her bed for the last time. It irked her not to be up and about, and she accused the doctor the family brought in of not knowing his business. There was marketing to do, and friends to call on, and work to get through with. When friends and relatives began calling on her, she was annoyed. Making out that she was really sick! Old Mrs Kurtz, who is seventy-two, visited her on the last day, and when she left, Aunt Ida looked after her pityingly. 'Poor Cora,' she said, 'she's failin', ain't she?'

HOW TO LISTEN TO A PLAY

Practically all the people I know who write plays want to read them to me. Furthermore, they do read them to me. I don't know why they select me to read plays to, because I am a very bad listener indeed, one of the worst listeners in the United States. I am always waiting for people to stop talking, or reading plays, so that I can talk, or read plays. Unfortunately, I have no plays to read to people (although I am always planning to write some) and, at forty, I do not talk as fast as I used to, or get into it as quickly, so that people with plays under their arms, or in their hip pockets, or even just vaguely outlined in their minds, get the jump on me. It is in the lobby of a hotel which I shall call the Cherokee that I am most often trapped by play readers. I frequently wander into the lobby looking for my hat or overcoat, which I am in the habit of forgetting and leaving there. Play readers seem to know this, for they are generally lurking near where I have left my hat or coat, waiting to pounce. They pounce very fast. 'Listen!' a play reader will say, confronting me without even a hallo or a how-are-you. 'The action takes place in a roadside hot-dog stand, with the usual what's-its-names and so-and-sos scattered here and there, a gasoline pump down right, and a cabin or two on the backdrop. Ella is this girl in charge of the stand; she is pretty, charming, and intelligent but can't get away from the stand to go to school or anything on account of her paralysed mother, who is paralysed but sinister, and very strong – she's the menace, see, but she doesn't come on until later. Ella is arranging the salt and mustard and what's-this on the counter when Harry comes on. Ella: "Hallo, Harry." Harry: "Hallo, Ella." You can see they are in love—'

'Who can?' I used to ask, bitterly, or 'How can you?', but I gave that up because interruptions other than 'That's fine', 'Swell' and the like are lost on people who read plays to you. What I usually do now is find a comfortable chair, lean back, close my eyes, put an index finger alongside one cheek, and, frowning slightly, pretend to be engrossed. It used to be difficult to do this for more than one act without dozing, but now I can do it for all three, saying 'That's fine' or 'Swell' at intervals, although I haven't actually taken in a word. A semi-doze, which even now I occasionally lapse into, is worse than complete sleep, because one finds oneself, in a semi-doze, now and then answering questions in the script. For instance, this question occurred in the second act of a play a woman was reading to me recently: 'How've you been, Jim?' 'Fine,' I answered, coming out of my doze without quite knowing where I was. 'How've *you* been?' That was a terrible moment for both of us, but I got out of it some way.

Some play readers buy you drinks while you listen, but you can't count on it, and it really isn't a good idea to drink during the reading of a three-act play, because it takes about an hour and a half to read a three-act play and you can get pretty cock-eyed in an hour and a half, especially if you are keeping your mind a blank. Many a time I have walked unsteadily out of the Cherokee at three-thirty in the afternoon, drunk as a lord, with nothing left to do but go to my apartment and go to sleep. As a rule, on these occasions I wake up about ten-thirty p.m. having accomplished nothing and with the whole heavy dull night ahead of me. Play readers don't care about that. They are selfish people.

I can think of no plays, no matter how fine, from *Macbeth* to *What Price Glory?*, that I would like to have read to me. I like to see them played or to read them myself, but I have never liked having *anything* read to me (the italics have been mine since I was a little boy). But no playwright will turn his play over to you (or at least he won't to me) so that it can be read alone and at your convenience. Playwrights like to read their plays aloud, because they think you will miss the full rich flavour of certain scenes if they don't. They do not seem to realise that a woman reading a man's part, or a man reading a woman's part, is not only dull but ineffective; but I do, I realise it.

Seven or eight years ago, when I first started in listening to plays, I would actually absorb the sense of the first few scenes before my mind began to wander and my eyes to rove. It really is advisable to comprehend a little of what has been read to you, because the moment is bound to come when the man or woman actually finishes the thing and stops reading. Then he or she is going to say, 'Well, what do you think of the character of Rose?' The only thing to say to this is 'I think the character of Rose is fine. You've got her down beautifully'; then you can go back quickly to the first scene of the first act (the one you listened to) and dwell on that. No playwright wants to dwell very long with you on the first scene of his first act (they are always crazy about their second and third acts), but if you are adroit enough, you can always work back to that first scene no matter what the playwright wants to have your opinion on. 'That', you can say of the second or third act, 'is perfect as it stands, perfect. I wouldn't change a line. Nor would I in that magnificent first scene where Ella and Harry discover they are in love.' Etc., etc.

It is useless to rely on some friend, wandering around the lobby, to extricate you from your predicament. I've tried that and it only caused more anguish. Once, when a playwright was slowly nearing his second-act curtain (where Harry and Ella rediscover that they are in love, or discover that they are not in love, or are in love with someone else, as the play may be), I slyly signalled a friend to come to my rescue. He walked over to where the playwright and I were sitting. 'Good Lord!' I cried, jumping to my feet and facing the newcomer. 'I completely forgot about you! We're late now, aren't we? We'll have to hurry!' He stared at me. 'Late for what? Hurry where?' he asked. I had a frightful time getting out of that.

If the play reader is bad, the plot outliner is even worse, because you don't have to meet the eyes of the reader, he being intent on his manuscript, but you can't get away from the eyes of the outliner. He usually begins something like this: 'There's this girl, see, and the guy, and her paralysed mother, who she suspects knows where she has hidden the franchise and naturally doesn't want Ella to leave the room because he'll get it. She knows that Ella is in love with Ella – I mean Harry, the fellow, see? – but the old girl sees through him even if she doesn't, only she can't talk, she can't speak, see, and let the girl know, let Ella know her suspicions.' Even if you listen with intense concentration, you can't follow the plot of a plot outliner. It gets more and more involved as it goes along and is bound to be filled with such terms as 'upstage' and 'downstage', which I always get mixed up so that I don't know where I am, or where Ella is or the old lady.

I am trying to be kind and considerate to everybody, out of repentance for the life I have led, but some day a play reader or a plot outliner is going to push me too far and I am going to get up in the middle of the first scene and scream. I am going to scream until the manager comes. I am going to scream until the ambulance and the police and the photographers come. I don't care how much people may talk.

I WENT TO SULLIVANT

I was reminded the other morning – by what, I don't remember and it doesn't matter – of a crisp September morning last year when I went to the Grand Central to see a little boy of ten get excitedly on a special coach that was to take him to a boys' school somewhere north of Boston. He had never been away to school before. The coach was squirming with youngsters; you could tell, after a while, the novitiates, shining and tremulous and a little awed, from the more aloof boys, who had been away to school before, but they were all very much alike at first glance. There was for me (in case you thought I was leading up to that) no sharp feeling of old lost years in the tense atmosphere of that coach, because I never went away to a private school when I was a little boy. I went to Sullivant School in Columbus. I thought about it as I walked back to my hotel.

Sullivant was an ordinary public school, and yet it was not like any other I have ever known of. In seeking an adjective to describe the Sullivant School of my years – 1900 to 1908 – I can only think of 'tough'. Sullivant School was tough. The boys of Sullivant came mostly from the region around Central Market, a poorish district with many coloured families and many white families of the labouring class. The school district also included a number of homes of the upper classes because, at the turn of the century, one or two old residential streets still lingered near the shouting and rumbling of the market, reluctant to surrender their fine old houses to the encroaching rabble of commerce, and become (as, alas, they now have) mere vulgar business streets.

I remember always, first of all, the Sullivant baseball team. Most grammar-school baseball teams are made up of boys in the seventh and eighth grades, or they were in my day, but with Sullivant it was different. Several of its best players were in the fourth grade, known to the teachers of the school as the Terrible Fourth. In that grade you first encountered fractions and long division, and many pupils lodged there for years, like logs in a brook. Some of the more able baseball-players had been in the fourth grade for seven or eight years. Then, too, there were a number of boys, most of them coloured (about half of the pupils at Sullivant were coloured), who had not been in the class past the normal time but were nevertheless deep in their teens. They had avoided starting to school – by eluding the truant officer – until they were ready to go into long pants, but he always got them in the end. One or two of these fourth-graders were seventeen or eighteen years old, but the dean of the squad was a tall, husky young man of twenty-two who was in the fifth grade (the teachers of the third and fourth had got tired of having him around as the years rolled along and had pushed him on). His name was Dana Waney and he had a moustache. Don't ask me why his parents allowed him to stay in school so long. There were many mysteries at Sullivant that were never cleared up. All I know is why he kept on in school and didn't go to work: he liked playing on the baseball team, and he had a pretty easy time in class, because the teachers had given up asking him any questions at all years before. The story was that he had answered but one question in the seventeen years he had been going to classes at Sullivant and that was 'What is one use of the comma?' 'The commy', said Dana, embarrassedly unsnarling his long legs from beneath a desk much too low for him, 'is used to shoot marbles with.' ('Commies' was our word for those cheap, ten-for-a-cent marbles, in case it wasn't yours.)

The Sullivant School baseball team of 1905 defeated several high-school teams in the city and claimed the high-school championship of the state, to which title it had, of course, no technical right. I believe the boys could have proved their moral right to the championship, however, if they had been allowed to go out of town and play all the teams they challenged, such as the powerful Dayton and Toledo nines, but their road season was called off after a terrific fight that occurred during a game in Mt Sterling, or Piqua, or Zenia – I can't remember which. Our first baseman – Dana Waney – crowned the umpire with a bat during an altercation over a called strike and the fight was on. It took place in the fourth inning, so of course the game was never finished (the battle continued on down into the business section of the town and raged for hours, with much destruction of property), but since

Sullivant was ahead at the time 17 to 0 there could have been no doubt as to the outcome. Nobody was killed. All of us boys were sure our team could have beaten Ohio State University that year, but they wouldn't play us; they were scared.

Waney was by no means the biggest or toughest guy on the grammar-school team; he was merely the oldest, being about a year the senior of Floyd, the coloured centre-fielder, who could jump five feet straight into the air without taking a running start. Nobody knew – not even the Board of Education, which once tried to find out – whether Floyd was Floyd's first name or his last name. He apparently only had one. He didn't have any parents, and nobody, including himself, seemed to know where he lived. When teachers insisted that he must have another name to go with Floyd, he would grow sullen and omin-ous and they would cease questioning him, because he was a dangerous scholar in a schoolroom brawl, as Mr Harrigan, the janitor, found out one morning when he was called in by a screaming teacher (all our teachers were women) to get Floyd under control after she had tried to whip him and he had begun to take the room apart, beginning with the desks. Floyd broke into small pieces the switch she had used on him (some said he also ate it; I don't know, because I was home sick at the time with mumps or something). Harrigan was a burly, iron-muscled janitor, a man come from a long line of coal-shov-ellers, but he was no match for Floyd, who had, to be sure, the considerable advantage of being more aroused than Mr Harri-gan when their fight started. Floyd had him down and was sit-ting on his chest in no time, and Harrigan had to promise to be good and to say 'Dat's what Ah get' ten times before Floyd would let him up.

I don't suppose I would ever have got through Sullivant School alive if it hadn't been for Floyd. For some reason he appointed himself my protector, and I needed one. If Floyd was known to be on your side, nobody in the school would dare be 'after' you and chase you home. I was one of the ten or fifteen male pupils in Sullivant School who always, or almost always, knew their lessons, and I believe Floyd admired the mental prowess of a youngster who knew how many continents there were and whether or not the sun was inhabited. Also, one time when it came my turn to read to the class – we used to take turns reading American history aloud – I came across the word 'Duquesne' and knew how to pronounce it. That charmed Floyd, who had been slouched in his seat idly following the printed page of his worn and pencilled textbook. 'How you know dat was Dukane, boy?' he asked me after class. 'I don't know,' I said. 'I just knew it.' He looked at me with round eyes. 'Boy, dat's sump'n,' he said. After that, word got around that Floyd would beat the tar out of anybody that messed around me. I wore glasses from the time I was eight and I knew my les-sons, and both of those things were considered pretty terrible at Sullivant. Floyd had one idiosyncrasy. In the early nineteen-hundreds, long warm furry gloves that came almost to your elbows were popular with boys, and Floyd had one of the biggest pairs in school. He wore them the year around.

Dick Peterson, another coloured boy, was an even greater

figure on the baseball team and in the school than Floyd was. He had a way in the classroom of blurting out a long deep rolling 'beee – eee – ahhhh!' for no reason at all. Once he licked three boys his own size single-handed, really single-handed, for he fought with his right hand and held a mandolin in his left hand all the time. It came out uninjured. Dick and Floyd never met in mortal combat, so nobody ever knew which one could 'beat', and the scholars were about evenly divided in their opinions. Many a fight started among them after school when that argument came up. I think school never let out at Sullivant without at least one fight starting up, and sometimes there were as many as five or six raging between the corner of Oak and Sixth Streets and the corner of Rich and Fourth Streets, four blocks away. Now and again virtually the whole school turned out to fight the Catholic boys of the Holy Cross Academy in Fifth Street near Town, for no reason at all – in winter with snowballs and iceballs, in other seasons with fists, brickbats, and clubs. Dick Peterson was always in the van,

yelling, singing, beeee-ahing, whirling all the way around when he swung with his right or (if he hadn't brought his mandolin) his left and missed. He made himself the pitcher on the baseball team because he was the captain. He was the captain because everybody was afraid to challenge his self-election, except Floyd. Floyd was too lazy to pitch and he didn't care who was captain, because he didn't fully comprehend what that meant. On one occasion, when Earl Battec, a steam-fitter's son, had shut out Mound Street School for six innings without a hit, Dick took him out of the pitcher's box and went in himself. He was hit hard and the other team scored, but it didn't make much difference, because the margin of Sullivant's victory was so great. The team didn't lose a game for five years to another grammar school. When Dick Peterson was in the sixth grade, he got into a saloon brawl and was killed.

When I go back to Columbus I always walk past Sullivant School. I have never happened to get there when classes were letting out, so I don't know what the pupils are like now. I am sure there are no more Dick Petersons and no more Floyds, unless Floyd is still going to school there. The play yard is still entirely bare of grass and covered with gravel, and the sycamores still line the curb between the schoolhouse fence and the Oak Street car line. A street-car line running past a schoolhouse is a dangerous thing as a rule, but I remember no one being injured while I was attending Sullivant. I do remember, however, one person who came very near being injured. He was a motorman on the Oak Street line, and once when his car stopped at the corner of Sixth to let off passengers, he yelled at Chutey Davidson, who played third base on the ball team, and was a member of the Terrible Fourth, to get out of the way. Chutey was a white boy, fourteen years old, but huge for his age, and he was standing on the tracks, taking a chew of tobacco. 'Come ahn down offa that car an' I'll knock your block off!' said Chutey, in what I can only describe as a Sullivant tone of voice. The motorman waited until Chutey moved slowly off the tracks; then he went on about his business. I think it was lucky for him that he did. There were boys in those days.

SNAPSHOT OF A DOG

I ran across a dim photograph of him the other day, going through some old things. He's been dead twenty-five years. His name was Rex (my two brothers and I named him when we were in our early teens) and he was a bull terrier. 'An American bull terrier', we used to say, proudly; none of your English bulls. He had one brindle eye that sometimes made him look like a clown and sometimes reminded you of a politician with derby hat and cigar. The rest of him was white except for a brindle saddle that always seemed to be slipping off and a brindle stocking on a hind leg. Nevertheless, there was a nobility about him. He was big and muscular and beautifully made. He never lost his dignity even when trying to accomplish the extravagant tasks my brothers and myself used to set for him. One of these was the bringing of a ten-foot wooden rail into the yard through the back gate. We would throw it out into the alley and tell him to go get it. Rex was as powerful as a wrestler, and there were not many things that he couldn't manage somehow to get hold of with his great jaws and lift or drag to wherever he wanted to put them, or wherever we wanted them put. He would catch the rail at the balance and lift it clear of the ground and trot with great confidence toward the gate. Of course, since the gate was only four feet wide or so, he couldn't bring the rail in broadside. He found that out when he got a few terrific jolts, but he wouldn't give up. He finally figured out how to do it, by dragging the rail, holding onto one end, growling. He got a great, wagging satisfaction out of his work. We used to bet kids who had never seen Rex in action that he could catch a baseball thrown as high as they could throw it. He almost never let us down. Rex could hold a baseball with ease in his mouth, in one cheek, as if it were a chew of tobacco.

He was a tremendous fighter, but he never started fights. I don't believe he liked to get into them, despite the fact that he came from a line of fighters. He never went for another dog's throat but for one of its ears (that teaches a dog a lesson), and he would get his grip, close his eyes, and hold on. He could hold on for hours. His longest fight lasted from dusk until almost pitch-dark, one Sunday. It was fought in East Main Street in Columbus with a large, snarly nondescript that belonged to a big coloured man. When Rex finally got his ear grip, the brief whirlwind of snarling turned to screeching. It was frightening to listen to and to watch. The Negro boldly picked the dogs up somehow and began swinging them around his head, and finally let them fly like a hammer in a hammer throw, but although they landed ten feet away with a great plump, Rex still held on.

The two dogs eventually worked their way to the middle of the car tracks, and after a while two or three streetcars were held up by the fight. A motorman tried to pry Rex's jaws open with a switch rod; somebody lighted a fire and made a torch of a stick and held that to Rex's tail, but he paid no attention. In the end, all the residents and storekeepers in the neighbourhood were on hand, shouting this, suggesting that. Rex's joy of battle, when battle was joined, was almost tranquil. He had a kind of pleasant expression during fights, not a vicious one, his eyes closed in what would have seemed to be sleep had it not been for the turmoil of the struggle. The Oak Street Fire Department finally had to be sent for – I don't know why nobody thought of it sooner. Five or six pieces of apparatus arrived, followed by a battalion chief. A hose was attached and a powerful stream of water was turned on the dogs. Rex held on for several moments more while the torrent buffeted him about like a log in a freshet. He was a hundred yards away from where the fight started when he finally let go.

The story of that Homeric fight got all around town, and some of our relatives looked upon the incident as a blot on the family name. They insisted that we get rid of Rex, but we were very happy with him, and nobody could have made us give him up. We would have left town with him first, along any road there was to go. It would have been different, perhaps, if he had ever started fights, or looked for trouble. But he had a gentle disposition. He never bit a person in the ten strenuous years that he lived, nor ever growled at anyone except prowlers. He killed cats, that is true, but quickly and neatly and without especial malice, the way men kill certain animals. It was the only thing he did that we could never cure him of doing. He never killed, or even chased, a squirrel. I don't know why. He had his own philosophy about such things. He never ran barking after wagons or automobiles. He didn't seem to see the idea in pursuing something you couldn't catch, or something you couldn't do anything with, even if you did catch it. A wagon was one of the things he couldn't tug along with his mighty jaws, and he knew it. Wagons, therefore, were not a part of his world.

Swimming was his favourite recreation. The first time he ever saw a body of water (Alum Creek), he trotted nervously along the steep bank for a while, fell to barking wildly, and finally plunged in from a height of eight feet or more. I shall always remember that shining, virgin dive. Then he swam upstream and back just for the pleasure of it, like a man. It was fun to see him battle upstream against a stiff current, struggling and growling every foot of the way. He had as much fun in the water as any person I have known. You didn't have to throw a stick in the water to get him to go in. Of course, he would bring back a stick to you if you did throw one in. He would even have brought back a piano if you had thrown one in.

That reminds me of the night, way after midnight, when he went a-roving in the light of the moon and brought back a small chest of drawers that he found somewhere – how far from the house nobody ever knew; since it was Rex, it could easily have been half a mile. There were no drawers in the chest when he got it home, and it wasn't a good one – he hadn't taken it out of anybody's house; it was just an old cheap piece that somebody had abandoned on a trash heap. Still, it was something he wanted, probably because it presented a nice problem in transportation. It tested his mettle. We first knew about his achievement when, deep in the night, we heard him trying to get the chest up onto the porch. It sounded as if two or three people were trying to tear the house down. We came downstairs and turned on the porch light. Rex was on the top step trying to pull the thing up, but it had caught somehow and he was just holding his own. I suppose he would have held his own till dawn if we hadn't helped him. The next day we carted the chest miles away and threw it out. If we had thrown it out in a nearby alley, he would have brought it home again, as a small token of his integrity in such matters. After all, he had been taught to carry heavy wooden objects about, and he was proud of his prowess.

I am glad Rex never saw a trained police dog jump. He was just an amateur jumper himself, but the most daring and tenacious I have ever seen. He would take on any fence we pointed out to him. Six feet was easy for him, and he could do eight by making a tremendous leap and hauling himself over finally by his paws, grunting and straining; but he lived and died without knowing that twelve- and sixteen-foot walls were too much for him. Frequently, after letting him try to go over one for a while, we would have to carry him home. He would never have given up trying.

There was in his world no such thing as the impossible. Even death couldn't beat him down. He died, it is true, but only, as one of his admirers said, after 'straight-arming the death angel' for more than an hour. Late one afternoon he wandered home, too slowly and too uncertainly to be the Rex that had trotted briskly homeward up our avenue for ten years. I think we all knew when he came through the gate that he was dying. He had apparently taken a terrible beating, probably from the owner of some dog that he had got into a fight with. His head and body were scarred. His heavy collar with the teeth marks of many a battle on it was awry; some of the big brass studs in it were sprung loose from the leather. He licked at our hands and, staggering, fell, but got up again. We could see that he was looking for someone. One of his three masters was not home. He did not get home for an hour. During that hour the bull terrier fought against death as he had fought against the cold, strong current of Alum Creek, as he had fought to climb twelve-foot walls. When the person he was waiting for did come through the gate, whistling, ceasing to whistle, Rex walked a few wabbly paces toward him, touched his hand with his muzzle, and fell down again. This time he didn't get up.

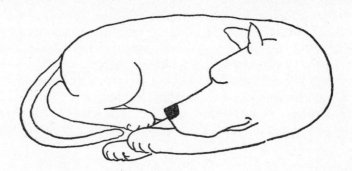

A DOZEN DISCIPLINES

Mrs Dorothea Brande, whose theory of how to get to Italy I discussed in the preceding pages [of *Let Your Mind Alone*], has a chapter in her *Wake Up and Live!* which suggests twelve specific disciplines. The purpose of these disciplines, she says, is to make our minds keener and more flexible. I'll take them up in order and show why it is no use for Mrs Brande to try to sharpen and limber up my mind, if these disciplines are all she has to offer. I quote them as they were quoted in a Simon & Schuster advertisement for the book, because the advertisement puts them more succinctly than Mrs Brande does herself.

'1. Spend one hour a day without speaking except in answer to direct questions.'

No hour of the day goes by that I am not in some minor difficulty which could easily become major if I did not shout for help. Just a few hours ago, for example, I found myself in a dilemma that has become rather familiar about my house: I had got tied up in a typewriter ribbon. The whole thing had come unwound from the spool and was wound around me.

American male tied up in typewriter ribbon

What started as an unfortunate slip of the hand slowly grew
into an enormous involvement. To have gone a whole hour
waiting for someone to show up and ask me a question could
not conceivably have improved my mind. Two minutes of
silence now and then is all right, but that is as far as I will go.

'2. Think one hour a day about one subject exclusively.'

Such as what, for example? At forty-two, I have spent a great
many hours thinking about all sorts of subjects, and there is
not one of them that I want to go back to for a whole hour. I can
pretty well cover as much of any subject as I want to in fifteen
minutes. Sometimes in six. Furthermore, it would be impossible for me, or for Mrs Brande, or for Simon & Schuster to
think for an hour exclusively on one subject. What is known as
'psychological association' would be bound to come into the
thing. For instance, let us say that I decide to think for a solid
hour about General Grant's horse (as good a subject as any at a
time when practically all subjects are in an unsettled state).
The fact that it is General Grant's horse would remind me of
General Grant's beard and that would remind me of Charles
Evans Hughes and that would remind me of the NRA. And so it
would go. If I resolutely went back to General Grant's horse
again, I would, by association, begin thinking about General
Lee's horse, which was a much more famous horse, a horse
named Traveller. I doubt if Mrs Brande even knows the name of
General Grant's horse, much less enough about it to keep her
mind occupied for sixty minutes. I mean sixty minutes of real
constructive thinking that would get her somewhere. Sixty
minutes of thinking of any kind is bound to lead to confusion
and unhappiness.

'3. Write a letter without using the first person singular.'

What for? To whom? About what? All I could possibly think
of to write would be a letter to a little boy telling him how to
build a rabbit hutch, and I don't know how to build a rabbit
hutch very well. I never knew a little boy who couldn't tell me
more about building a rabbit hutch than I could tell him.
Nobody in my family was ever good at building rabbit hutches,
although a lot of us raised rabbits. I have sometimes wondered
how we managed it. I remember the time that my father offered
to help me and my two brothers build a rabbit hutch out of
planks and close-meshed chicken wire. Somehow or other he

got inside of the cage after the wire had been put up around the sides and over the top, and he began to monkey with the stout door. I don't know exactly what happened, but he shut the door and it latched securely and he was locked in with the rabbits. The place was a shambles before he got out, because nobody was home at the time and he couldn't get his hand through the wire to unlatch the door. He had his derby on in the hutch all during his captivity and that added to his discomfiture. I remember, too, that we boys (we were not yet in our teens) didn't at first know what the word 'hutch' meant, but we had got hold of a pamphlet on the subject, which my brother Herman read with great care. One sentence in the pamphlet read, 'The rabbits' hutches should be cleaned thoroughly once a week.' It was this admonition which caused my brother one day to get each of the astonished rabbits down in turn and wash its haunches thoroughly with soap and water.

No, I do not think that anybody can write a letter without using the first person singular. Even if it could be done, I see no reason to do it.

'4. Talk for fifteen minutes without using the first person.' No can do. No going to *try* to do, either. You can't teach an old egoist new persons.

'5. Write a letter in a placid, successful tone, sticking to facts about yourself.'

Now we're getting somewhere, except that nothing is more stuffy and conceited-sounding than a 'placid, successful tone'. The way to write about yourself is to let yourself go. Build it up, exaggerate, make yourself out a person of importance. Fantasy is the food for the mind, not facts. Are we going to wake up and live or are we going to sit around writing factual letters in a placid, successful tone?

'6. Pause before you enter any crowded room and consider your relations with the people in it.'

Now, Mrs Brande, if I did that there would be only about one out of every thirty-two crowded rooms I approached that I would ever enter. I always shut my mind and plunge into a crowded room as if it were a cold bath. That gives me and everybody in the room a clean break, a fresh starting point. There is no good in rehashing a lot of old relations with people. The longer I paused outside a crowded room and thought about my relations with the people in it, the more inclined I would be to go back to the checkroom and get my hat and coat and go home. That's the best place for a person, anyway – home.

'7. Keep a new acquaintance talking, exclusively about himself.'

And then tiptoe quietly away. He'll never notice the difference.

'8. Talk exclusively about yourself for fifteen minutes.'

And see what happens.

'9. Eliminate the phrases "I mean" and "As a matter of fact" from your conversation.'

Okie-dokie.

'10. Plan to live two hours a day according to a rigid time schedule.'

Well, I usually wake up at nine in the morning and lie there till eleven, if that would do. Of course, I could *plan* to do a lot of different things over a period of two hours, but if I actually started out to accomplish them I would instantly begin to worry about whether I was going to come out on the dot in the end and I wouldn't do any of them right. It would be like waiting for the pistol shot during the last quarter of a close football game. This rule seems to me to be devised simply to make men irritable and jumpy.

'11. Set yourself twelve instructions on pieces of paper, shuffle them, and follow the one you draw. Here are a few samples: "Go twelve hours without food." "Stay up all night and work." "Say nothing all day except in answer to questions."'

In that going twelve hours without food, do you mean I can have drinks? Because if I can have drinks, I can do it easily. As for staying up all night and working, I know all about that: that simply turns night into day and day into night. I once got myself into such a state staying up all night that I was always having orange juice and boiled eggs at twilight and was just ready for lunch after everybody had gone to bed. I had to go away to a sanitarium to get turned around. As for saying nothing all day except in answer to questions, what am I to do if a genial colleague comes into my office and says, 'I think your mother is one of the nicest people I ever met' or 'I was thinking about giving you that twenty dollars you lent me'? Do I just stare at him and walk out of the room? I lose enough friends, and money, the way it is.

'12. Say "Yes" to every reasonable request made of you in the course of one day.'

All right, start making some. I can't think of a single one off-hand. The word 'reasonable' has taken a terrible tossing around in my life – both personal and business. If you mean watering the geraniums, I'll do that. If you mean walking around Central Park with you for the fresh air and exercise, you are crazy.

Has anybody got any more sets of specific disciplines? If anybody has, they've got to be pretty easy ones if I am going to wake up and live. It's mighty comfortable dozing here and waiting for the end.

NINE NEEDLES

One of the more spectacular minor happenings of the past few years which I am sorry that I missed took place in the Columbus, Ohio, home of some friends of a friend of mine. It seems that a Mr Albatross, while looking for something in his medicine cabinet one morning, discovered a bottle of a kind of patent medicine which his wife had been taking for a stomach ailment. Now, Mr Albatross is one of those apprehensive men who are afraid of patent medicines and of almost everything else. Some weeks before, he had encountered a paragraph in a Consumers' Research bulletin which announced that this particular medicine was bad for you. He had thereupon ordered his wife to throw out what was left of her supply of the stuff and never buy any more. She had promised, and here now was another bottle of the perilous liquid. Mr Albatross, a man given to quick rages, shouted the conclusion of the story at my friend: 'I threw the bottle out the bathroom window and the medicine chest after it!' It seems to me that must have been a spectacle worth going a long way to see.

I am sure that many a husband has wanted to wrench the family medicine cabinet off the wall and throw it out the window, if only because the average medicine cabinet is so filled with mysterious bottles and unidentifiable objects of all kinds that it

'And the medicine chest after it!'

is a source of constant bewilderment and exasperation to the American male. Surely the British medicine cabinet and the French medicine cabinet and all the other medicine cabinets must be simpler and better ordered than ours. It may be that the American habit of saving everything and never throwing anything away, even empty bottles, causes the domestic medicine cabinet to become as cluttered in its small way as the American attic becomes cluttered in its major way. I have encountered few medicine cabinets in this country which were not pack-jammed with something between a hundred and fifty and two hundred different items, from dental floss to boracic acid, from razor blades to sodium perborate, from adhesive tape to coconut oil. Even the neatest wife will put off clearing out the medicine cabinet on the ground that she has something else to do that is more important at the moment, or more diverting. It was in the apartment of such a wife and her husband that I became enormously involved with a medicine cabinet one morning not long ago.

I had spent the weekend with this couple – they live on East Tenth Street near Fifth Avenue – such a weekend as left me reluctant to rise up on Monday morning with bright and shining face and go to work. They got up and went to work, but I didn't. I didn't get up until about two-thirty in the afternoon. I had my face all lathered for shaving and the washbowl was full of hot water when suddenly I cut myself with the razor. I cut my ear. Very few men cut their ears with razors, but I do, possibly because I was taught the old Spencerian free-wrist movement by my writing teacher in the grammar grades. The ear bleeds rather profusely when cut with a razor and is difficult to get at. More angry than hurt, I jerked open the door of the medicine cabinet to see if I could find a styptic pencil and out fell, from the top shelf, a little black paper packet containing nine needles. It seems that this wife kept a little paper packet containing nine needles on the top shelf of the medicine cabinet. The packet fell into the soapy water of the washbowl, where the paper rapidly disintegrated, leaving nine needles at large in the bowl. I was, naturally enough, not in the best condition, either physical or mental, to recover nine needles from a washbowl. No gentleman who has lather on his face and whose ear is bleeding is in the best condition for anything, even something involving the handling of nine large blunt objects.

It did not seem wise to me to pull the plug out of the washbowl and let the needles go down the drain. I had visions of clogging up the plumbing system of the house, and also a vague fear of causing short circuits somehow or other (I know very little about electricity and I don't want to have it explained to me). Finally, I groped very gently around the bowl and eventually had four of the needles in the palm of one hand and three in the palm of the other – two I couldn't find. If I had thought quickly and clearly, I wouldn't have done that. A lathered man whose ear is bleeding and who has four wet needles in one hand and three in the other may be said to have reached the lowest known point of human efficiency. There is nothing he can do but stand there. I tried transferring the needles in my left hand to the palm of my right hand, but I couldn't get them off my left hand. Wet needles cling to you. In the end, I wiped the needles off onto a bathtowel which was hanging on a rod above the bathtub. It was the only towel that I could find. I had to dry my hands afterward on the bathmat. Then I tried to find the needles in the towel. Hunting for seven needles in a bathtowel is the most tedious occupation I have ever engaged in. I could find only five of them. With the two that had been left in the bowl, that meant there were four needles in all missing – two in the washbowl and two others lurking in the towel or lying in the bathtub under the towel. Frightful thoughts came to me of what might happen to anyone who used that towel or washed his face in the bowl or got into the tub, if I didn't find the missing needles. Well, I didn't find them. I sat down on the edge of the tub to think, and I decided finally that the only thing to do was wrap up the towel in a newspaper and take it away with me. I also decided to leave a note for my friends explaining as clearly as I could that I was afraid there were two needles in the bathtub and two needles in the washbowl, and that they better be careful.

I looked everywhere in the apartment, but I could not find a pencil, or a pen, or a typewriter. I could find pieces of paper, but nothing with which to write on them. I don't know what gave me the idea – a movie I had seen, perhaps, or a story I had read – but I suddenly thought of writing a message with a lipstick. The wife might have an extra lipstick lying around and, if so, I concluded it would be in the medicine cabinet. I went back to the medicine cabinet and began poking around in it for a lipstick. I saw what I thought looked like the metal tip of one, and I got two fingers around it and began to pull gently – it was under a lot of things. Every object in the medicine cabinet began to slide. Bottles broke in the washbowl and on the floor; red, brown, and white liquids spurted; nail files, scissors, razor blades, and miscellaneous objects sang and clattered and tinkled. I was covered with perfume, peroxide, and cold cream.

It took me half an hour to get the debris all together in the middle of the bathroom floor. I made no attempt to put anything back in the medicine cabinet. I knew it would take a steadier hand than mine and a less shattered spirit. Before I went away (only partly shaved) and abandoned the shambles, I left a note saying that I was afraid there were needles in the bathtub and the washbowl and that I had taken their towel and that I would call up and tell them everything – I wrote it in iodine with the end of a toothbrush. I have not yet called up, I am sorry to say. I have neither found the courage nor thought up the words to explain what happened. I suppose my friends believe that I deliberately smashed up their bathroom and stole their towel. I don't know for sure, because they have not yet called me up, either.

SULI SULI

I always try to answer Abercrombie & Fitch's questions (in their advertisements) the way they obviously want them answered, but usually, if I am to be honest with them and with myself, I must answer them in a way that would not please Abercrombie & Fitch. While that company and I have always nodded and smiled pleasantly enough when we met, we have never really been on intimate terms, mainly because we have so little in common. For one thing, I am inclined to be nervous and impatient, whereas Abercrombie & Fitch are at all times composed and tranquil. In the case of a man and a woman this disparity in temperament sometimes works out all right, but with Abercrombie & Fitch and me it is different: neither one of us is willing to submerge any part of his personality in the other, or compromise in matters of precedent, habit, or tradition. Yet in spite of all the natural barriers between Abercrombie & Fitch and myself, we are drawn to each other by a curious kind of fascination, or perhaps it is only me who is drawn to them. Not long ago I dropped in at their store to browse around among all the glittering objects, when suddenly I was faced by a tall and courteous but firm clerk who asked me if there was anything he could do for me. I said instantly, 'I want to buy a javelin.'

Now, it is true that I have always wanted to buy a javelin, because I have always wanted to see how far I could throw one, but two things had, up to the day I am telling about, kept me from going ahead with the thing. First, I had been afraid that I would not be able to throw a javelin as far as Babe Didrikson used to throw one, and I knew that the discovery that a woman could throw anything further than I could throw it would have a depressing effect on me and might show up in my work and in my relationships with women. Second, I did not know how Abercrombie & Fitch, of whom I have ever been slightly in awe, would take my wanting to buy a javelin. They are, to be sure, a very courteous firm, but they have a way of looking at you sometimes as if you had left your spoon in your coffee cup.

However, all my fears and uncertainties were beside the point, because here I was, finally asking Abercrombie & Fitch for a javelin.

'A *javelin?*' said Abercrombie & Fitch (I shall call the clerk that), and I knew instantly from his inflection that he did not think I should have a javelin and, furthermore, I knew that I was not going to get one. Somehow or other it was not the thing for a tall, thin man in a blue suit to come in and ask for a javelin. I was, naturally, embarrassed. 'I – uh – yes, I had thought some of purchasing a javelin,' I said. 'It's for a rather – a sort of special use, in a way, I mean, what I want, of course, is *two* javelins; that is, a *pair* of javelins, so that I could cross them, like oars, you know, or guns, above a mantelpiece. I have oars and guns, of course, but I – I——' Beyond this I could not go with a story that was becoming more and more difficult for me and, I daresay, stranger and stranger to Abercrombie & Fitch. A kind of feverish high note was in my voice, a note that always betrays me when I am lying. 'I am very sorry,' said Abercrombie & Fitch, his eyebrows raised slightly, 'but we have no javelins in stock.' He paused; then, 'I could order one for you.' He knew, you see, that I really only wanted one; my story about wanting two had not fooled him for a minute. I think he also suspected that I wanted to find out whether I could throw the thing as far as Babe Didrikson. Abercrombie & Fitch can read me like a book; I don't know just why. I told the clerk to let it go, not to bother, and to cover my confusion I bought a set of lawn bowls, although I have no lawn that I could possibly use for bowls. I believe the clerk knew that, too.

But I am straying from the point I began with, about Abercrombie & Fitch's questions, the ones I can almost never answer the way they would like to have them answered. Take the one recently printed in an advertisement in *The New Yorker*. Under a picture of a man fishing in a stream were these words: 'Can't you picture yourself in the middle of the stream with the certain knowledge that a wise old trout is hiding under a ledge and defying you to tempt him with your skilfully cast fly?' My answer, of course, is 'No.' Especially if I am to be equipped the way the gentleman in the illustration is equipped: with rod, reel, line, net, hip boots, felt hat, and pipe. They might just as well add a banjo and a parachute to my equipment, along with a grandfather's clock, for with anything at all to handle in the middle of a rushing brook I would drown faster than you could say 'J. Robins'. The wise old trout would have the laugh of his life, especially when I began to cast. I tried casting in a stream only twice, and the first time I caught a tree and the second time I barely missed landing one of a group of picnickers. Therefore, I cannot agree with Abercrombie & Fitch's ad when it says further: 'Words are poor to express the delight of just handling a beautiful rod with a sweet-singing reel and a line that seems alive as it answers the flick of your wrist.' It seems alive all right, but it answers different men in different ways; with me, it is surly to the point of impudence. No, I am afraid I am not going to send for one of the fly-fishing catalogues the company advertised or drop in and look at their 'complete trout outfits'. Abercrombie & Fitch would know, just glancing at me, that I would be at the mercy of the complete trout outfit, and of the trout, too – if they were brave enough to come at me when I went down in a tangle of rod, reel, line, net, boots, pipe, and hat.

I am sorry to have to say this to Abercrombie & Fitch, but fishing of any kind is something I don't like to picture myself doing. Oh, I've tried fishing of various kinds, but I never seemed to get the hang of any of them. I still remember a gay fishing party I went on with a lot of strong men and beautiful girls, when I was still fairly strong myself. It was a fine day and it was a pleasant creek and the fish were biting. Everybody except me was pulling in perch and pickerel, or whatever they were – all fish look exactly alike to me. I kept pulling out of the water an aged and irritable turtle. No matter where I moved along the bank or where I dropped my line, I would hook the turtle. Nobody else got him, but I got him variously, by the leg, the back of his shell, and his belly, but never securely; he wouldn't swallow the hook, he just monkeyed with it. He would always drop back into the water as I was about to haul him in. I didn't really want him, but I wanted to get him out of the way. It furnished a great deal of amusement for everybody, except me and the turtle. Another time I went fishing on Lake Skaneateles with a group of people, including a lovely young woman named Sylvia. On this occasion I actually did hook a fish, even before anybody else had a bite, and I brought it into the rowboat with a great plop. Then, not having had any experience with a caught fish, I didn't know what to do with it. I had had some vague idea that a fish died quietly and with dignity as soon as it was flopped into a boat, but that, of course, was an erroneous idea. It leaped about strenuously. I got pretty far away from it and stared at it. The young lady named Sylvia finally grabbed it expertly and slapped it into insensibility against the sides and bottom of the boat. I think it was perhaps then that I decided to go in for javelin-throwing and began to live with the dream of being able to throw a javelin further than Babe Didrikson. A man never completely gets over the chagrin and shock of having a woman handle for him the fish he has caught.

As for deep-sea fishing, you and I – and Abercrombie & Fitch – know that an old turtle-catcher is not going to be able to cope with a big-game fish that fights you for ten or twelve hours and drags you from Miami to Jacksonville. Every time I read an article about deep-sea fishing I realise more thoroughly than ever that, as far as I am concerned, all the sailfish and tuna and tarpon are as safe as if they were in bank vaults. In a recent piece in *Esquire*, Mr Hemingway tells about a man who hooked an eighty-pound fish which, before the man could pull it in, was grabbed up far below the surface by some unknown monster of the deep, who took a bite at it and let it go. When the original quarry was brought up, it was seen that the other fish had 'squeezed it and held it so that every bit of the insides of the fish had been crushed out while the huge fish moved off with the eighty-pound fish in its mouth.' 'What size of a fish would that be?' Mr Hemingway asks. He needn't look at me. I do not stick in boats very well, particularly if they are being jerked around by a fish that has another fish in its mouth, and I never expect to get near enough to their habitat to make even a wild guess as to their size.

Then there was an article I came on in, of all magazines, the *East African Annual*, for 1934–5, called 'Sea Fishing Off the Coast of Kenya', by Mr Hugh Copley. In Africa, you can get big, strong black natives (Suli Suli they are called, I think) to go out in a boat with you, but I am afraid they would only hamper and confuse me. Mr Copley lists the names of the big fish you can pursue along the Kenya coast, giving first the English name, then the technical name, and then the native, or Swahili, name. The list begins this way: 'I. The sailfish (Istiophorus gladius), Suli Suli. 2. Herschel's spearfish (Makaira herscheli), Suli Suli.' The predicaments that an American, and I mean me, might get into deep-sea fishing with a native that called everything Suli Suli are infinite. I don't even like to think about it. Nor would I ever be able to look after my tackle the way Mr Copley says it should be looked after, because I would never get anything else done except that, day in and day out. He writes, 'Lines must be dried every evening. Reels taken apart and greased. When the fishing trip is over soak all the lines for a night in fresh water and then dry thoroughly for a whole day. All hooks, wire traces, must be greased; gaffs cleaned with emery paper and then greased. The rod should be examined for broken whippings; these replaced and the rod given three coats of best coach varnish.' I have a pretty vivid picture of what I would look like after all that greasing and regreasing. And then, of course, the whole thing falls down for me when it comes to the three coats that have to be put on the rod. I might go into Abercrombie & Fitch and ask for a javelin, as indeed I did, but I would never think of going up to one of their clerks and saying, 'I should like to buy a bottle of coach varnish.' I have no idea what would happen, but the episode would be, I am sure, most unfortunate.

HIGHBALL FLAGS

It is a matter of common knowledge among smart sea-going gentlemen (if you keep your eyes open, you will have read about it) that the ubiquitous yachtsman can now purchase a cocktail flag for his pleasure craft. To quote an item I recently read on the subject, the flag has 'a red glass on a white field' and it means 'We're serving drinks.' When it is flown upside down, it means 'Who has a drink?' I know very little about the ways of yachtsmen but I have always thought of them as rather reserved, aristocratic gentlemen, not given to garrulity in flags, or to announcing private parties with flags, or to public – or rather high-seas – cadging of drinks with flags. Apparently I was wrong. The ancient practice of sailing a ship, once the prerogative of strong, silent men of retiring disposition, appears about to go the way the canoe went when the ukulele came along. The advent of the cocktail flag, with its strange device, seems likely to lead to a deplorable debasing of the dignity of yachts and yachting – and yachtsmen. Surely anybody will have to be allowed aboard who can climb aboard – that is, when the flag is flown right side up; and certainly all sorts of common and vulgar boats are going to come alongside, roaring and singing (and possibly carrying nothing but gin and ginger ale), when the flag is flown upside down. It is too late now to do anything about this except to suggest some further flag signals; as long as yachts are going in for open drinking and carousing, they may as well do the thing up right. No yachting party which has gone so far as to fly the cocktail flag upside down is going to be satisfied with that. There are a lot of other things the people on board will want to say, after they have run out of drinks and are bawling for more, and an array of signals for these other things might just as well be arranged now. I have a few suggestions to make along this line; yachtsmen can take them or they can let them alone. What I propose is a series of highball flags, to be run up after the cocktail flag has been struck.

Flag No. 1: The head of a woman, blue, on a white field. This means 'My wife is the finest little girl in all the world.'

Flag No. 2: Steel-coloured fist on a crimson field. This means 'I can lick any other yachtsman within sight of this flag.' If flown upside down, this means the same thing plus 'with one hand tied behind me'.

Flag No. 3: Six grey fists rampant on a dark-blue field. This means 'Let's all go over and beat hell out of the Monarch of Bermuda' (or whatever other large, peaceful ship is lying nearest the yacht and the other yachts it is talking to).

Flag No. 4: White zigzag lightning flash on black field. This means 'Let's have one more quick one and then we'll get the hell out of here.'

Flag No. 5: Large scarlet question mark on white field. This means 'Has anybody got a tenor on board?'

Flag No. 6: Red eye and pendent pear-shaped silver tear on black field. This means 'You're bes' frien' ev' had.' If hung upside down, it means 'You're fines' ship ev' seen.'

Flag No. 7: White stocking on scarlet field. This means 'We want women!'

Flag No. 8: Black zigzag lightning flash on white field. This means the same as No. 4.

Flag No. 9: Four male heads, white eyes, red, open mouths, on smoky-grey field. This means, if right side up, 'Let's sing "Honey, Honey, Bless Your Heart"'; if upside down, 'Let's sing "I

'Honey, Honey, Bless Your Heart'

had a Dream, Dear".' There should be one hundred other similar flags for the one hundred other songs men sing when in their cups, and also, of course, a black flag with a white thumb centred; when hung with the thumb pointing up, this means 'O.K., you pitch it'; when hung with the thumb pointing down, it means 'No, not "Sweet Adeline"!'

Flag No. 111: Horizontal white line on sable field. This means 'I got to lie down.'

Flag No. 112: A large plain yellow flag. This means 'I said I got to lie *down*!'

If you have any other ideas, don't send them to me, for my yellow flag is flying, upside down (which means 'Gone to bed'); send them to Abercrombie & Fitch. They are selling the cocktail flags, or anyway they have them in stock.

THE HIDING GENERATION

One afternoon almost two years ago, at a cocktail party (at least, this is the way I have been telling the story), an eager middle-aged woman said to me, 'Do you belong to the Lost Generation, Mr T?' and I retorted, coldly and quick as a flash, 'No, Madam, I belong to the Hiding Generation.'

As a matter of fact, no woman ever asked me such a question at a cocktail party or anywhere else. I thought up the little dialogue one night when I couldn't sleep. At the time, my retort seemed pretty sharp and satirical to me, and I hoped that some day somebody *would* ask me if I belonged to the Lost Generation, so that I could say no, I belonged to the Hiding Generation. But nobody ever has. My retort, however, began working in the back of my mind. I decided that since I was apparently never going to get a chance to use it as repartee, I ought to do something else with it, if only to get it out of the back of my mind. About ten months ago I got around to the idea of writing a book called *The Hiding Generation*, which would be the story of my own intellectual conflicts, emotional disturbances, spiritual adventures, and journalistic experiences, something in the manner of Malcolm Cowley's *Exile's Return* or Vincent Sheean's *Personal History*. The notion seemed to me a remarkably good one, and I was quite excited by it. I bought a new typewriter ribbon and a ream of fresh copy paper; I sharpened a dozen pencils; I got a pipe and tobacco. Then I sat down at the typewriter, lighted my pipe, and wrote on a sheet of paper '*The Hiding Generation*, by James Thurber.' That was as far as I got, because I discovered that I could not think of anything else to say. I mean anything at all.

Thus passed the first five or six hours of my work on the book. In the late afternoon some people dropped in for cocktails, and I didn't get around to the book again for two more days. Then I found that I still didn't have anything to say. I wondered if I had already said everything I had to say, but I decided, in looking over what I had said in the past, that I really hadn't ever said anything. This was an extremely

Some people dropped in for cocktails

depressing thought, and for a while I considered going into some other line of work. But I am not fitted for any other line of work, by inclination, experience, or aptitude. There was consequently nothing left for me but to go back to work on *The Hiding Generation*. I decided to 'write it in my mind', in the manner of Arnold Bennett (who did practically all of *The Old Wives' Tale* in his head), and this I devoted myself to for about seven months. At length I sat down at the typewriter once more, and there I was again, tapping my fingers on the table, lighting and relighting my pipe, getting up every now and then for a drink of water. I figured finally that maybe I had better make an outline of the book; probably all the writers I had in mind – and there was a pretty big list of them now, including Walter Duranty and Negley Farson – had made an outline of what they were going to say, using Roman numerals for the main divisions and small letters 'a' and 'b', etc., for the subdivisions. So I set down some Roman numerals and small letters on a sheet of paper. First I wrote 'I. Early Youth'. I could think of no subdivisions to go under that, so I put down 'II. Young Manhood'. All I could think of to go under that was 'a. Studs Lonigan'. Obviously that wouldn't do, so I tore up the sheet of paper and put the whole thing by for another week.

During that week I was tortured by the realisation that I couldn't think of anything important that had happened to me up to the time I was thirty-three and began raising Scotch terriers. The conviction that nothing important had happened to me until I was thirty-three, that I had apparently had no intellectual conflicts or emotional disturbances, or anything, reduced me to such a state of dejection that I decided to go to Bridgeport for a few days and stay all alone in a hotel room. The motivation behind this decision is still a little vague in my mind, but I think it grew out of a feeling that I wasn't worthy of going away to Florida or Bermuda or Nassau or any other nice place. I had Bridgeport 'coming to me', in a sense, as retribution for my blank youth and my blank young manhood. In the end, of course, I did not go to Bridgeport. I took a new sheet of paper and began another outline.

This time I started out with 'I. University Life. a. Intellectual Conflicts'. No other workable subdivisions occurred to me. The only Emotional Disturbance that came to my mind was unworthy of being incorporated in the book, for it had to do with the moment, during the Phi Psi May Dance of 1917, when I knocked a fruit salad onto the floor. The incident was as bald as that, and somehow I couldn't correlate it with anything. To start out with such an episode and then just leave it hanging in the air would not give the reader anything to get his teeth into. Therefore I concentrated on 'Intellectual Conflicts', but I could not seem to call up any which had torn my mind asunder during my college days. yet there *must* have been some. I made a lot of little squares and circles with a pencil for half an hour, and finally I remembered one intellectual conflict – if you could call it that. It was really only an argument I had had with a classmate at Ohio State University named Arthur Spencer, about *Tess of the D'Urbervilles*. I had taken the view that the hero of the book was not justified in running away to South America and abandoning Tess simply because she had been indiscreet in her youth. Spencer, on the other hand, contended the man was fully justified, and that he (Spencer) would have run away to South America and left Tess, or any other woman, under the circumstances – that is, if he had had the money. As a matter of fact, Spencer settled down in East Liverpool, Ohio, where he is partner in his father's hardware store, and married a very nice girl named Sarah Gammadinger, who had been a Kappa at Ohio State.

I came to the conclusion finally that I would have to leave my university life out of the book, along with my early youth and young manhood. Therefore, my next Roman numeral, which would normally have been IV, automatically became I. I placed after it the words 'Paris: A New World. a. Thoughts at Sea'. It happened that upon leaving the university, in 1918, I went to Paris as a clerk, Grade B, in the American Embassy. In those days I didn't call it clerk, Grade B, I called it attaché, but it seemed to me that the honest and forceful thing to do was to tell the truth. The book would have more power and persuasion if I told the truth – providing I could remember the truth. There was a lot I couldn't remember, I found out in trying to. For instance, I had put down 'Thoughts at Sea' after 'a' because I couldn't recall anything significant that had happened to me during the five months I spent in Washington, D.C., before sailing for France. (Furthermore, it didn't seem logical to put a subdivision called 'Washington Days' under a general heading called 'Paris: A New World'.) Something, of course, must have happened to me in Washington, something provocative or instructive, something that added to my stature, but all that comes back to me is a series of paltry little memories. I remember there was a waitress in the Post Café, at the corner of Thirteenth and E Streets, whose last name was Rabbit. I've forgot her first name and even what she looked like, but her last name was Rabbit. A Mrs Rabbit. Then there was the flu epidemic, during which I gargled glycothymoline three times a day. All the rest has gone from me.

I found I could remember quite a lot about my days at sea on my way to Paris: A New World. In the first place, I had bought a box of San Felice cigars to take with me on the transport, but I was seasick all the way over and the cigars were smoked by a man named Ed Corcoran, who travelled with me. He was not sick a day. I believe he said he had never been sick a day in his life. Even some of the sailors were sick, but not Corcoran. No, sir. He was constantly in and out of our stateroom, singing, joking, smoking my cigars. The other thing I remembered about the voyage was that my trunk and suitcase failed to get on the ship; they were put by mistake on some other ship – the *Minnetonka*, perhaps, or the *Charles O. Sprague*, a coastwise fruit steamer. In any case, I didn't recover them until May, 1920, in Paris, and the Hershey bars my mother had packed here and there in both the trunk and the suitcase had melted and were all over everything. All my suits were brown, even the grey one. But I am anticipating myself. All this belongs under 'Paris: A New World. b. Paris'.

I was just twenty-five when I first saw Paris, and I was still a little sick. Unfortunately, when I try to remember my first impressions of Paris and the things that happened to me, I get them mixed up with my second trip to Paris, which was seven years later, when I was feeling much better and really got around more. On that first trip to Paris I was, naturally enough, without any clothes, except what I had on, and I had to outfit myself at once, which I did at the Galeries Lafayette. I paid $.4.75 in American money for a pair of B.V.D.s. I remember that, all right. Nothing else comes back to me very clearly; everything comes back to me all jumbled up. I tried about five times to write down a comprehensive outline of my experiences in Paris: A New World, but the thing remained sketchy and trivial. If there was any development in my character or change in my outlook on life during that phase, I forget just where it came in and why. So I cut out the Paris interlude.

I find, in looking over my accumulation of outlines, that my last attempt to get the volume started began with the heading 'I. New York Again: An Old World'. This was confusing, because it could have meaning and pertinence only if it followed the chapter outlined as 'Paris: A New World', and that had all been eliminated along with my Early Youth, Young Manhood, and University Days. Moreover, while my life back in New York must have done a great deal to change my character, viewpoint, objectives, and political ideals, I forget just exactly how this happened. I am the kind of man who should keep notes about such things. If I do not keep notes, I simply cannot remember a thing. Oh, I remember odds and ends, as you have seen, but they certainly would not tie up into anything like a moving chronicle of a man's life, running to a hundred and fifty thousand words. If they ran to twenty-five hundred words, I would be going good. Now, it's a funny thing: catch me in a drawing-room, over the coffee and liqueurs, particularly the Scotch-and-sodas, and I could hold you, or at least keep talking to you, for five or six hours about my life, but somebody would have to take down what I said and organise it into a book. When I sit down to *write* the story of my life, all I can think of is Mrs Rabbit, and the Hershey bars, and the B.V.D.s that came within two bits of costing five bucks. That is, of course, until I get up to the time when I was thirty-three and began raising Scotch terriers. I can put down all of that, completely and movingly, without even making an outline. Naturally, as complete and as moving as it might be, it would scarcely make a biography like, say, Negley Farson's, and it certainly would not sustain so pretentious a title as *The Hiding Generation*. I would have to publish it as a pamphlet entitled *The Care and Training of Scotch Terriers*. I am very much afraid that that is what my long arduous struggle to write the story of my life is going to come down to, if it is going to come down to anything.

Well, all of us cannot write long autobiographies. But *almost* all of us can.

A COUPLE OF HAMBURGERS

It had been raining for a long time, a slow, cold rain falling out of iron-coloured clouds. They had been driving since morning and they still had a hundred and thirty miles to go. It was about three o'clock in the afternoon. 'I'm getting hungry,' she said. He took his eyes off the wet, winding road for a fraction of a second and said, 'We'll stop at a dog-wagon.' She shifted her position irritably. 'I wish you wouldn't call them dog-wagons,' she said. He pressed the klaxon button and went around a slow car. 'That's what they are,' he said. 'Dog-wagons.' She waited a few seconds. '*Decent* people call them *diners*,' she told him, and added, 'Even if you call them diners, I don't like them.' He speeded up a hill. 'They have better stuff than most restaurants,' he said. 'Anyway, I want to get home before dark and it takes too long in a restaurant. We can stay our stomachs with a couple hamburgers.' She lighted a cigarette and he asked her to light one for him. She lighted one deliberately and handed it to him. 'I wish you wouldn't say "stay our stomachs",' she said. 'You know I hate that. It's like "sticking to your ribs". You say that all the time.' He grinned. 'Good old American expressions, both of them,' he said. 'Like sow belly. Old pioneer term, sow belly.' She sniffed. 'My ancestors were pioneers, too. You don't have to be vulgar just because you were a pioneer.' 'Your ancestors never got as far west as mine did,' he said. 'The real pioneers travelled on their sow belly and got somewhere.' He laughed loudly at that. She looked out at the wet trees and signs and telephone poles going by. They drove on for several miles without a word; he kept chortling every now and then.

'What's that funny sound?' she asked, suddenly. It invariably made him angry when she heard a funny sound. 'What funny sound?' he demanded. 'You're always hearing funny sounds.' She laughed briefly. 'That's what you said when the bearing burned out,' she reminded him. 'You'd never have noticed it if it hadn't been for me.' 'I noticed it, all right,' he said. 'Yes,' she said. 'When it was too late.' She enjoyed bring-

ing up the subject of the burned-out bearing whenever he got
to chortling. 'It was too late when *you* noticed it, as far as that
goes,' he said. Then, after a pause, 'Well, what does it sound
like *this* time? All engines make a noise running, you know.' 'I
know all about that,' she answered. 'It sounds like – it sounds
like a lot of safety pins being jiggled around in a tumbler.' He
snorted. 'That's your imagination. Nothing gets the matter
with a car that sounds like a lot of safety pins. I happen to
know that.' She tossed away her cigarette. 'Oh, sure,' she said.
'You always happen to know everything.' They drove on in
silence.

'I want to stop somewhere and get something to eat!' she
said loudly. 'All right, all right!' he said. 'I been watching for a
dog-wagon, haven't I? There hasn't been any. I can't make you a
dog-wagon.' The wind blew rain in on her and she put up the
window on her side all the way. 'I won't stop at just any old
diner,' she said. 'I won't stop unless it's a cute one.' He looked
around at her. 'Unless it's a *what* one?' he shouted. 'You know
what I mean,' she said. 'I mean a decent, clean one where they
don't slosh things at you. I hate to have a lot of milky coffee
sloshed at me.' 'All right,' he said. 'We'll find a cute one, then.

You pick it out. I wouldn't know. I might find one that was cunning but not cute.' That struck him as funny and he began to chortle again. 'Oh, shut up,' she said.

Five miles further along they came to a place called Sam's Diner. 'Here's one,' he said, slowing down. She looked it over. 'I don't want to stop there,' she said. 'I don't like the ones that have nicknames.' He brought the car to a stop at one side of the road. 'Just what's the matter with the ones that have nicknames?' he asked with edgy, mock interest. 'They're always Greek ones,' she told him. 'They're always Greek ones,' he repeated after her. He set his teeth firmly together and started up again. After a time, 'Good old Sam, the Greek,' he said, in a singsong. 'Good old Connecticut Sam Beardsley, the Greek.' 'You didn't see his name,' she snapped. 'Winthrop, then,' he said. 'Old Samuel Cabot Winthrop, the Greek dog-wagon man.' He was getting hungry.

On the outskirts of the next town she said, as he slowed down, 'It looks like a factory kind of town.' He knew that she meant she wouldn't stop there. He drove on through the place. She lighted a cigarette as they pulled out into the open again. He slowed down and lighted a cigarette for himself. 'Factory kind of town than *I* am!' he snarled. It was ten miles before they came to another town. 'Torrington,' he growled. 'Happen to know there's a dog-wagon here because I stopped in it once with Bob Combs. Damn cute place, too, if you ask me.' 'I'm not asking you anything,' she said, coldly. 'You think you're *so* funny. I think I know the one you mean,' she said, after a moment. 'It's right in the town and it sits at an angle from the road. They're never so good, for some reason.' He glared at her and almost ran up against the curb. 'What the hell do you mean "sits at an angle from the road"?' he cried. He was very hungry now. 'Well, it isn't silly,' she said, calmly. 'I've noticed the ones that sit at an angle. They're cheaper, because they fitted them into funny little pieces of ground. The big ones parallel to the road are the best.' He drove right through Torrington, his lips compressed. 'Angle from the *road*, for God's sake!' he snarled, finally. She was looking out her window.

On the outskirts of the next town there was a diner called The Elite Diner. 'This looks—' she began. 'I see it, I see it!' he said. 'It doesn't happen to look any cuter to me than any goddam—' she cut him off. 'Don't be such a sorehead, for Lord's sake,' she said. He pulled up and stopped beside the diner, and turned on her. 'Listen,' he said, grittingly, 'I'm going to put down a couple of hamburgers in this place even if there isn't one single inch of chintz or cretonne in the whole—' 'Oh, be still,' she said. 'You're just hungry and mean like a child. Eat your old hamburgers, what do I care?' Inside the place they sat down on stools and the counterman walked over to them, wiping up the counter top with a cloth as he did so. 'What'll it be, folks?' he said. 'Bad day, ain't it? Except for ducks.' 'I'll have a couple of—' began the husband, but his wife cut in. 'I just want a pack of cigarettes,' she said. He turned around slowly on his stool and stared at her as she put a dime and a nickel in the cigarette machine and ejected a package of Lucky Strikes. He turned to the counterman again. 'I want a couple of hamburgers,' he said. 'With mustard and lots of onion. *Lots* of onion!' She hated onions. 'I'll wait for you in the car,' she said. He didn't answer and she went out.

He finished his hamburgers and his coffee slowly. It was terrible coffee. Then he went out to the car and got in and drove off, slowly humming 'Who's Afraid of the Big Bad Wolf?'. After a mile or so, 'Well,' he said, 'what was the matter with the Elite Diner, milady?' 'Didn't you *see* that cloth the man was wiping the counter with?' she demanded. 'Ugh!' She shuddered. 'I didn't happen to want to eat any of the counter,' he said. He laughed at that comeback. 'You didn't even notice it,' she said. 'You never notice anything. It was filthy.' 'I noticed they had some damn fine coffee in there,' he said. 'It was swell.' He knew she loved good coffee. He began to hum his tune again; then he whistled it; then he began to sing it. She did not show her annoyance, but she knew that he knew she was annoyed. 'Will you be kind enough to tell me what time it is?' she asked. 'Big *bad* wolf, big *bad* wolf – five minutes o' five – tum-dee-*doo*-dee-dum-m-m.' She settled back in her seat and took a cigarette from her case and tapped it on the case. 'I'll wait till we get home,' she said. 'If you'll be kind enough to speed up a little.' He drove on at the same speed. After a time he gave up the 'Big Bad Wolf' and there was deep silence for two miles. Then suddenly he began to sing, very loudly, '*H-A-double-R-I-G-A-N spells Harrr*-i-gan—' She gritted her teeth. She hated that worse than any of his songs except 'Barney Google'. He would go on to 'Barney Google' pretty soon, she knew. Suddenly she leaned slightly forward. The straight line of her lips began to curve up ever so slightly. She heard the safety pins in the tumbler again. Only now they were louder, more insistent, ominous. He was singing too loud to hear them. 'Is a *name* that *shame* has never been con-*nec*-ted with – *Harrr*-i-gan, that's *me*!.' She relaxed against the back of the seat, content to wait.

THE SECRET LIFE OF WALTER MITTY

'We're going through!' The Commander's voice was like thin ice breaking. He wore his full-dress uniform, with the heavily braided white cap pulled down rakishly over one cold grey eye. 'We can't make it, sir. It's spoiling for a hurricane, if you ask me.' 'I'm not asking you, Lieutenant Berg,' said the Commander. 'Throw on the power lights! Rev her up to 8,500! We're going through!' The pounding of the cylinders increased: ta-pocketa-pocketa-pocketa-*pocketa-pocketa*. The Commander stared at the ice forming on the pilot window. He walked over and twisted a row of complicated dials. 'Switch on No. 8 auxiliary!' he shouted. 'Switch on No. 8 auxiliary!' repeated Lieutenant Berg. 'Full strength to No. 3 turret!' shouted the Commander. 'Full strength in No. 3 turret!' The crew, bending to their various tasks in the huge, hurtling eight-engined Navy hydroplane, looked at each other and grinned. 'The Old Man'll get us through,' they said to one another. 'The Old Man ain't afraid of Hell!' . . .

'Not so fast! You're driving too fast!' said Mrs Mitty. 'What are you driving so fast for?'

'Hmm?' said Walter Mitty. He looked at his wife, in the seat beside him, with shocked astonishment. She seemed grossly unfamiliar, like a strange woman who had yelled at him in a crowd. 'You were up to fifty-five,' she said. 'You know I don't like to go more than forty. You were up to fifty-five.' Walter Mitty drove on toward Waterbury in silence, the roaring of the SN202 through the worst storm in twenty years of Navy flying fading in the remote, intimate airways of his mind. 'You're tensed up again,' said Mrs Mitty. 'It's one of your days. I wish you'd let Dr Renshaw look you over.'

Walter Mitty stopped the car in front of the building where his wife went to have her hair done. 'Remember to get those overshoes while I'm having my hair done,' she said. 'I don't need overshoes,' said Mitty. She put her mirror back into her bag. 'We've been all through that,' she said, getting out of the car. 'You're not a young man any longer.' He raced the engine a little. 'Why don't you wear your gloves? Have you lost your gloves?' Walter Mitty reached in a pocket and brought out the gloves. He put them on, but after she had turned and gone into the building and he had driven on to a red light, he took them off again. 'Pick it up, brother!' snapped a cop as the light changed, and Mitty hastily pulled on his gloves and lurched ahead. He drove around the streets aimlessly for a time, and then he drove past the hospital on his way to the parking lot.

. . . 'It's the millionaire banker, Wellington McMillan,' said the pretty nurse. 'Yes?' said Walter Mitty, removing his gloves slowly. 'Who has the case?' 'Dr Renshaw and Dr Benbow, but there are two specialists here, Dr Remington from New York and Mr Pritchard-Mitford from London. He flew over.' A door opened down a long, cool corridor and Dr Renshaw came out. He looked distraught and haggard. 'Hallo, Mitty,' he said. 'We're having the devil's own time with McMillan, the millionaire banker and close personal friend of Roosevelt. Obstreosis of the ductal tract. Tertiary. Wish you'd take a look at him.' 'Glad to,' said Mitty.

In the operating room there were whispered introductions: 'Dr Remington, Dr Mitty. Mr Pritchard-Mitford, Dr Mitty.' 'I've read your book on streptothricosis,' said Pritchard-Mitford, shaking hands. 'A brilliant performance, sir.' 'Thank you,' said Walter Mitty. 'Didn't know you were in the States, Mitty,' grumbled Remington. 'Coals to Newcastle, bringing Mitford and me up here for a tertiary.' 'You are very kind,' said Mitty. A huge, complicated machine, connected to the operating table, with many tubes and wires, began at this moment to go pocketa-pocketa-pocketa. 'The new anaesthetiser is giving way!' shouted an intern. 'There is no one in the East who knows how to fix it!' 'Quiet, man!' said Mitty, in a low, cool voice. He sprang to the machine, which was now going pocketa-pocketa-queep-pocketa-queep. He began fingering delicately a row of glistening dials. 'Give me a fountain pen!' he snapped. Someone handed him a fountain pen. He pulled a faulty piston out of the machine and inserted the pen in its place. 'That will hold for ten minutes,' he said. 'Get on with the operation.' A nurse hurried over and whispered to Renshaw, and Mitty saw the man turn pale. 'Coreopsis has set in,' said Renshaw nervously. 'If you would take over, Mitty?' Mitty looked at him and at the craven figure of Benbow, who drank, and at the grave, uncertain faces of the two great specialists. 'If you wish,' he said. They slipped a white gown on him; he adjusted a mask and drew on thin gloves; nurses handed him shining . . .

'Back it up, Mac! Look out for that Buick!' Walter Mitty jammed on the brakes. 'Wrong lane, Mac,' said the parking-lot attendant, looking at Mitty closely. 'Gee. Yeh,' muttered Mitty. He began cautiously to back out of the lane marked 'Exit Only'. 'Leave her sit there,' said the attendant. 'I'll put her away.' Mitty got out of the car. 'Hey, better leave the key.' 'Oh,' said Mitty, handing the man the ignition key. The attendant vaulted into the car, backed it up with insolent skill, and put it where it belonged.

They're so damn cocky, thought Walter Mitty, walking along Main Street; they think they know everything. Once he had tried to take his chains off, outside New Milford, and he had got them wound around the axles. A man had had to come out in a wrecking car and unwind them, a young, grinning garageman. Since then Mrs Mitty always made him drive to a garage to have the chains taken off. The next time, he thought, I'll wear my right arm in a sling; they won't grin at me then. I'll have my right arm in a sling and they'll see I couldn't possibly take the chains off myself. He kicked at the slush on the sidewalk. 'Over-shoes,' he said to himself, and he began looking for a shoe store.

When he came out into the street again, with the overshoes in a box under his arm, Walter Mitty began to wonder what the other thing was his wife had told him to get. She had told him, twice, before they set out from their house for Waterbury. In a way he hated these weekly trips to town – he was always get-ting something wrong. Kleenex, he thought, Squibb's, razor blades? No. Toothpaste, toothbrush, bicarbonate, carborun-dum, initiative and referendum? He gave it up. But she would remember it. 'Where's the what's-its-name?' she would ask. 'Don't tell me you forgot the what's-its-name.' A newsboy went by shouting something about the Waterbury trial.

. . .'Perhaps this will refresh your memory.' The District Attorney suddenly thrust a heavy automatic at the quiet figure on the witness stand. 'Have you ever seen this before?' Walter Mitty took the gun and examined it expertly. 'This is my Webley-Vickers 50.80,' he said calmly. An excited buzz ran around the courtroom. The Judge rapped for order. 'You are a crack shot with any sort of firearms, I believe?' said the District

Attorney, insinuatingly. 'Objection!' shouted Mitty's attorney. 'We have shown that the defendant could not have fired the shot. We have shown that he wore his right arm in a sling on the night of the fourteenth of July.' Walter Mitty raised his hand briefly and the bickering attorneys were stilled. 'With any known make of gun,' he said evenly, 'I could have killed Gregory Fitzhurst at three hundred feet *with my left hand*.' Pandemonium broke loose in the courtroom. A woman's scream rose above the bedlam and suddenly a lovely, dark-haired girl was in Walter Mitty's arms. The District Attorney struck at her savagely. Without rising from his chair, Mitty let the man have it on the point of the chin. 'You miserable cur!' . . .

'Puppy biscuit,' said Walter Mitty. He stopped walking and the buildings of Waterbury rose up out of the misty courtroom and surrounded him again. A woman who was passing laughed. 'He said "Puppy biscuit",' she said to her companion. 'That man said "Puppy biscuit" to himself.' Walter Mitty hurried on. He went into an A. & P., not the first one he came to but a smaller one further up the street. 'I want some biscuit for small, young dogs,' he said to the clerk. 'Any special brand, sir?' The greatest pistol shot in the world thought a moment. 'It says "Puppies Bark for It" on the box,' said Walter Mitty.

His wife would be through at the hairdresser's in fifteen minutes, Mitty saw in looking at his watch, unless they had trouble drying it; sometimes they had trouble drying it. She didn't like to get to the hotel first; she would want him to be there waiting for her as usual. He found a big leather chair in the lobby, facing a window, and he put the overshoes and the puppy biscuit on the floor beside it. He picked up an old copy of *Liberty* and sank down into the chair. 'Can Germany Conquer the World Through the Air?' Walter Mitty looked at the pictures of bombing planes and of ruined streets.

. . . 'The cannonading has got the wind up in young Raleigh, sir,' said the Sergeant. Captain Mitty looked up at him through tousled hair. 'Get him to bed,' he said wearily. 'With the others. I'll fly alone.' 'But you can't, sir,' said the Sergeant anxiously. 'It takes two men to handle that bomber and the Archies are pounding hell out of the air. Von Richtman's circus is between here and Saulier.' 'Somebody's got to get that ammunition dump,' said Mitty. 'I'm going over. Spot of brandy?' He poured a drink for the Sergeant and one for himself. War thundered and whined around the dugout and battered at the door. There was a rending of wood and splinters flew through the room. 'A bit of a near thing,' said Captain Mitty carelessly. 'The box barrage is closing in,' said the Sergeant. 'We only live once, Sergeant,' said Mitty, with his faint, fleeting smile. 'Or do we?' He poured another brandy and tossed it off. 'I never see a man could hold his brandy like you, sir,' said the Sergeant. 'Begging your pardon, sir.' Captain Mitty stood up and strapped on his huge Webley-Vickers automatic. 'It's forty kilometres through hell, sir,' said the Sergeant. Mitty finished one last brandy. 'After all,' he said softly, 'What isn't?' The pounding of the cannon increased; there was the rat-tat-tatting of machine guns, and from somewhere came the menacing pocketa-pocketa-pocketa of the new flame-throwers. Walter Mitty walked to the door of the dugout humming 'Auprès de Ma Blonde'. He turned and waved to the Sergeant. 'Cheerio!' he said . . .

Something struck his shoulder. 'I've been looking all over this hotel for you,' said Mrs Mitty. 'Why do you have to hide in this old chair? How did you expect me to find you?' 'Things close in,' said Walter Mitty vaguely. 'What?' Mrs Mitty said. 'Did you get the what's-its-name? The puppy biscuit? What's in that box?' 'Overshoes,' said Mitty. 'Couldn't you have put them on in the store?' 'I was thinking,' said Walter Mitty. 'Does it ever occur to you that I am sometimes thinking?' She looked at him. 'I'm going to take your temperature when I get you home,' she said.

They went out through the revolving doors that made a faintly derisive whistling sound when you pushed them. It was two blocks to the parking lot. At the drugstore on the corner she said, 'Wait here for me. I forgot something. I won't be a minute.' She was more than a minute. Walter Mitty lighted a cigarette. It began to rain, rain with sleet in it. He stood up against the wall of the drugstore, smoking . . . He put his shoulders back and his heels together. 'To hell with the handkerchief,' said Walter Mitty scornfully. He took one last drag on his cigarette and snapped it away. Then, with that faint, fleeting smile playing about his lips, he faced the firing squad; erect and motionless, proud and disdainful, Walter Mitty the Undefeated, inscrutable to the last.

THE MACBETH MURDER MYSTERY

'It was a stupid mistake to make,' said the American woman I had met at my hotel in the English lake country, 'but it was on the counter with the other Penguin books – the little sixpenny ones, you know, with the paper covers – and I supposed of course it was a detective story. All the others were detective stories. I'd read all the others, so I bought this one without really looking at it carefully. You can imagine how mad I was when I found it was Shakespeare.' I murmured something sympathetically. 'I don't see why the Penguin-books people had to get out Shakespeare's plays in the same size and everything as the detective stories,' went on my companion. 'I think they have different-coloured jackets,' I said. 'Well, I didn't notice that,' she said. 'Anyway, I got real comfy in bed that night and all ready to read a good mystery story and here I had *The Tragedy of Macbeth* – a book for highschool students. Like *Ivanhoe*.' 'Or *Lorna Doone*,' I said. 'Exactly,' said the American lady. 'And I was just crazy for a good Agatha Christie, or something. Hercule Poirot is my favourite detective.' 'Is he the rabbity one?' I asked. 'Oh, no,' said my crime-fiction expert. 'He's the Belgian one. You're thinking of Mr Pinkerton, the one that helps Inspector Bull. He's good, too.'

Over her second cup of tea my companion began to tell the plot of a detective story that had fooled her completely – it seems it was the old family doctor all the time. But I cut in on her. 'Tell me,' I said. 'Did you read *Macbeth*?' '*I had* to read it,' she said. 'There wasn't a scrap of anything else to read in the whole room.' 'Did you like it?' I asked. 'No, I did not,' she said, decisively. 'In the first place, I don't think for a moment that Macbeth did it.' I looked at her blankly. 'Did what?' I asked. 'I don't think for a moment that he killed the King,' she said. 'I don't think the Macbeth woman was mixed up in it, either. You suspect them the most, of course, but those are the ones that are never guilty – or shouldn't be, anyway.' 'I'm afraid', I began, 'that I—' 'But don't you see?' said the American lady. 'It would spoil everything if you could figure out right away who did it.

Shakespeare was too smart for that. I've read that people never *have* figured out *Hamlet*, so it isn't likely Shakespeare would have made *Macbeth* as simple as it seems.' I thought this over while I filled my pipe. 'Who do you suspect?' I asked, suddenly. 'Macduff,' she said, promptly. 'Good God!' I whispered, softly.

'Oh, Macduff did it, all right,' said the murder specialist. 'Hercule Poirot would have got him easily.' 'How did you figure it out?' I demanded. 'Well,' she said, 'I didn't right away. At first I suspected Banquo. And then, of course, he was the second person killed. That was good right in there, that part. The person you suspect of the first murder should always be the second victim.' 'Is that so?' I murmured. 'Oh, yes,' said my informant. 'They have to keep surprising you. Well, after the second murder I didn't know *who* the killer was for a while.' 'How about Malcolm and Donalbain, the King's sons?' I asked. 'As I remember it, they fled right after the first murder. That looks suspicious.' 'Too suspicious,' said the American lady. 'Much too suspicious. When they flee, they're never guilty. You can count on that.' 'I believe,' I said, 'I'll have a brandy,' and I summoned the waiter. My companion leaned toward me, her eyes bright, her teacup quivering. 'Do you know who discovered Duncan's body?' she demanded. I said I was sorry, but I had forgotten. 'Macduff discovers it,' she said, slipping into the historical present. 'Then he comes running downstairs and shouts, "Confusion has broke ope the Lord's anointed temple" and "Sacrilegious murder has made his masterpiece" and on and on like that.' The good lady tapped me on the knee. 'All that stuff was *rehearsed*,' she said. 'You wouldn't say a lot of stuff like that, offhand, would you – if you had found a body?' She fixed me with a glittering eye. 'I—' I began. 'You're right!' she said. 'You wouldn't! Unless you had practised it in advance. "My God, there's a body in here!" is what an innocent man would say.' She sat back with a confident glare.

I thought for a while. 'But what do you make of the Third Murderer?' I asked. 'You know, the Third Murderer has puzzled *Macbeth* scholars for three hundred years.' 'That's because they never thought of Macduff,' said the American lady. 'It was Macduff, I'm certain. You couldn't have one of the victims murdered by two ordinary thugs – the murderer always has to be somebody important.' 'But what about the banquet scene?' I asked, after a moment. 'How do you account for Macbeth's guilty actions there, when Banquo's ghost came in and sat in his chair?' The lady leaned forward and tapped me on the knee again. 'There wasn't any ghost,' she said. 'A big, strong man like that doesn't go around seeing ghosts – especially in a brightly lighted banquet hall with dozens of people around. Macbeth was *shielding somebody!*' 'Who was he shielding?' I asked. 'Mrs Macbeth, of course,' she said. 'He thought she did it and he was going to take the rap himself. The husband always does that when the wife is suspected.' 'But what', I demanded, 'about the sleepwalking scene, then?' 'The same thing, only the other way around,' said my companion. 'That time *she* was shielding *him*. She wasn't asleep at all. Do you remember where it says, "Enter Lady Macbeth with a taper"?' 'Yes,' I said. 'Well, people who walk in their sleep *never carry lights!*' said my fellow-traveller. 'They have a second sight. Did you ever hear of a sleepwalker carrying a light?' 'No,' I said, 'I never did.' 'Well, then, she wasn't asleep. She was acting guilty to shield Macbeth.' 'I think', I said, 'I'll have another brandy,' and I called the waiter. When he brought it, I drank it rapidly and rose to go. 'I believe', I said, 'that you have got hold of something. Would you lend me that *Macbeth*? I'd like to look it over tonight. I don't feel, somehow, as if I'd ever really read it.' 'I'll get it for you,' she said. 'But you'll find that I am right.'

I read the play over carefully that night, and the next morning, after breakfast, I sought out the American woman. She was on the putting green, and I came up behind her silently and took her arm. She gave an exclamation. 'Could I see you alone?' I asked, in a low voice. She nodded cautiously and followed me to a secluded spot. 'You've found out something?' she breathed. 'I've found out', I said, triumphantly, 'the name of the murderer!' 'You mean it wasn't Macduff?' she said. 'Macduff is as innocent of those murders', I said, 'as Macbeth and the Macbeth woman.' I opened the copy of the play, which I had with me, and turned to Act II, Scene 2. 'Here', I said, 'you will see where Lady Macbeth says, "I laid their daggers ready. He could not miss 'em. Had he not resembled my father as he slept, I had done it." Do you see?' 'No,' said the American woman, bluntly, 'I don't.' 'But it's simple!' I exclaimed. 'I wonder I didn't see it years ago. The reason Duncan resembled Lady Macbeth's father as he slept is that *it actually was her father!*' 'Good God!' breathed my companion, softly. 'Lady Macbeth's father killed the King,' I said, 'and, hearing someone coming, thrust the body under the bed and crawled into the bed himself.' 'But', said the lady, 'you can't have a murderer who only appears in the story once. You can't have that.' 'I know that,' I said, and I turned to Act II, Scene 4. 'It says here, "Enter Ross with an old Man." Now, that old man is never identified and it is my contention he was old Mr Macbeth, whose ambition it was to make his daughter Queen. There you have your motive.' 'But even then,' cried the American lady, 'he's still a minor character!' 'Not', I said, gleefully, 'when you realise that he was also *one of the weird sisters in disguise!*' 'You mean one of the three witches?' 'Precisely,' I said. 'Listen to this speech of the old man's. "On Tuesday last, a falcon towering in her pride of place, was by a mousing owl hawk'd at and kill'd." Who does that sound like?' 'It sounds like the way the three witches talk,' said my companion, reluctantly. 'Precisely!' I said again. 'Well,' said the American woman, 'maybe you're right, but—' 'I'm sure I am,' I said. 'And do you know what I'm going to do now?' 'No,' she said. 'What?' 'Buy a copy of *Hamlet*,' I said, 'and solve *that*.' My companion's eyes brightened. 'Then', she said, 'you don't think Hamlet did it?' 'I am', I said, 'absolutely positive he didn't.' 'But who', she demanded, 'do you suspect?' I looked at her cryptically. 'Everybody,' I said, and disappeared into a small grove of trees as silently as I had come.

CARTOONS

'*Well it makes a difference to me!*'

'You and your premonitions!'

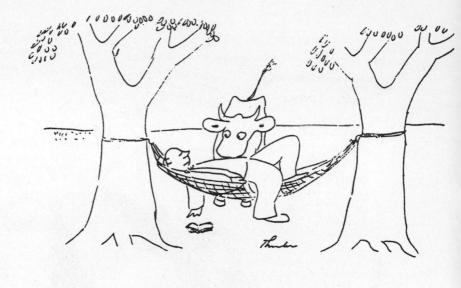

'Courting the Muse?'

'Perhaps this will refresh your memory'

'Do you ever have fears that you may cease to be
before your pen has gleaned your teeming brain?'

'I can't get in touch with your uncle, but there's a horse here that wants to say hallo'

'If I told you a dream I had about you, Mr Price, would you promise not to do anything about it unless you really want to?'

'The magic has gone out of my marriage.
Has the magic gone out of your marriage?'

'Hello, darling—wool gathering?'

'My wife wants to spend Halloween with her first husband'

'Go away, you look human!'

'He knows all about art, but he doesn't know what he likes.'

'Well, don't *come and look at the rainbow then, you big ape!*'

MEMOIRS OF A DRUDGE

Mr Thurber . . . went to Ohio State University for his formal education. His informal education included . . . drudgery on several newspapers – in Columbus, in New York, and in Paris.
– From *Horse Sense in American Humor*, by Walter Blair.

I don't know about that. There is, of course, a certain amount of drudgery in newspaper work, just as there is in teaching classes, tunnelling into a bank, or being President of the United States. I suppose that even the most pleasurable of imaginable occupations, that of batting baseballs through the windows of the R.C.A. Building, would pall a little as the days ran on. Seldom, it is true, do I gather my grandchildren about my knees and tell them tall tales out of my colourful years as a leg man, but I often sit in the cane-seated rocker on the back porch, thinking of the old days and cackling with that glee known only to ageing journalists. Just the other evening, when the womenfolks were washing up the supper dishes and setting them to dreen, they could hear me rocking back and forth and laughing to myself. I was thinking about the Riviera edition of the *Chicago Tribune* in southern France during the winter of 1925–6.

Seven or eight of us had been assigned to the task of getting out a little six-page newspaper, whose stories were set up in 10-point type, instead of the customary 8-point, to make life easier for everybody, including the readers. Most of our news came by wire from the Paris edition, and all we had to do was write headlines for it, a pleasurable occupation if you are not rushed, and we were never rushed. For the rest, we copied from the *Éclaireur de Nice et du Sud-Est*, a journal filled with droll and mystical stories, whose translation, far from being drudgery, was pure joy. Nice, in that indolent winter, was full of knaves and rascals, adventurers and impostors, *pochards* and *indiscrets*, whose ingenious exploits, sometimes in full masquerade costume, sometimes in the nude, were easy and pleasant to record.

We went to work after dinner and usually had the last chronicle of the diverting day written and ready for the lino-typers well before midnight. It was then our custom to sit around for half an hour, making up items for the society editor's column. She was too pretty, we thought, to waste the soft southern days tracking down the arrival of prominent persons on the Azure Coast. So all she had to do was stop in at the Ruhl and the Negresco each day and pick up the list of guests who had just registered. The rest of us invented enough items to fill up the last half of her column, and a gay and romantic caval-cade, indeed, infested the littoral of our imagination. 'Lieu-tenant General and Mrs Pendleton Gray Winslow', we would write, 'have arrived at their villa, Heart's Desire, on Cap d'Antibes, bringing with them their prize Burmese monkey, Thibault.' Or 'The Hon. Mr Stephen H. L. Atterbury, Chargé-d'Affaires of the American Legation in Peru, and Mrs Atterbury, the former Princess Ti Ling of Tibet, are motoring to Monte Carlo from Aix-en-Provence, where they have been visiting Mr Atterbury's father, Rear Admiral A. Watson Atterbury, U.S.N., retired. Mr Stephen Atterbury is the breeder of the famous Schnauzer-Pincer, Champion Adelbert von Weigengrosse of Tamerlane, said to be valued at $15,000.' In this manner we turned out, in no time at all, and with the expenditure of very little mental energy, the most glittering column of social notes in the history of the American newspaper, either here or abroad.

As the hour of midnight struck twice, in accordance with the dreamy custom of town and church clocks in southern France, and our four or five hours of drudgery were ending, the late Frank Harris would often drop in at the *Tribune* office, and we would listen to stories of Oscar Wilde, Walt Whitman, Bernard Shaw, Emma Goldman and Frank Harris. Thus ran the harsh and exacting tenor of those days of slavery.

It is true that the languorous somnolence of our life was occasionally broken up. This would happen about one night a week, around ten o'clock, when our French composing room went on strike. The printers and their foreman, a handsome, black-bearded giant of a man, whose rages resembled the mis-tral, wanted to set up headlines in their own easygoing way, using whatever size type was handiest and whatever space it would fit into most easily. That is the effortless hit-or-miss system which has made a crazy quilt of French newspaper headlines for two hundred years, and André and his men could not understand why we stubbornly refused to adopt so sane and simple a method. So now and then, when he couldn't stand our stupid and inviolable headline schedules any longer, André would roar into our little city room like a storm from the Alps. Behind him in the doorway stood his linotypers, with their hats and coats on. Since the Frenchmen could comprehend no English and spoke only *Niçois*, an argot entirely meaningless to us, our arguments were carried on in shouting and gesticulating and a great deal of waving of French and American newspapers in each other's faces. After a while all the combatants on both sides would adjourn to the bar next door, still yelling and gesturing, but after four or five rounds of beer we would fall to singing old Provençal songs and new American ones, and there would be a truce for another six or seven days, everybody going back to work, still singing.

On one of those nights of battle, song and compromise, several of us defenders of the immutable American headline went back to the bar after we had got the *Tribune* to press and sat up till dawn, drinking *grog américain*. Just as the sun came up, we got on a train for Cannes, where the most talked-about international struggle of the year was to take place that afternoon, the tennis match between Suzanne Lenglen and Helen Wills. As we climbed aboard, one of my colleagues, spoiling for an argument, declared that a French translation he had read of Edgar Allen Poe's 'The Raven' was infinitely superior to the poem in the original English. How we had got around to this curious subject I have no idea, but it seemed natural enough at the time. I remember that a young reporter named Middleton visited all the compartments on the train, demanding of their sleepy and startled French occupants if they did not believe that a raven was more likely to say *'Jamais plus'* than 'Nevermore'. He returned with the claim that our fellow-passengers to a man were passionately on the side of *'Jamais plus'*. So passed a night of drudgery in the fond, far-away days of the Third Republic and the Riviera edition of the *Chicago Tribune*.

We had the long days of warm blue weather for our own, to

climb the Corniche roads or wind up the mountain in a *char à bancs* to the magical streams and the million springtime flowers of St-Martin-Vésubie. Sometimes we sat the day out on the terrace of a restaurant overlooking the Bay of Angels and gave the tireless Albert suggestions as to where he might find Henry James. Albert was a young Englishman who did interviews for us with distinguished visitors to the Riviera, and he had got the curious idea that the celebrated novelist was hiding away in a *pension* somewhere between St Tropez and Mentone, rewriting *The Golden Bowl*. We decided that Albert had got his tip about the whereabouts of the great dead man from some ageing aunt who lived in the parlours and the gardens of the past. It was one way to spend an afternoon, sitting over our glasses of vermouth-cassis, bringing back to life the poor, sensitive creator of Peter Quint and Mme de Vionnet, figuring him lost and wandering, ever so wonderfully, somewhere among the bougainvillaea and the passionflowers. Thus in fancy and in dream passed the long days of warm blue weather.

Before going to France, I worked on the Columbus *Evening Dispatch*, a fat and amiable newspaper, whose city editor seldom knew where I was and got so that he didn't care. He had a glimpse of me every day at 9 a.m., arriving at the office, and promptly at ten he saw me leave it, a sheaf of folded copy paper in my pocket and a look of enterprise in my eye. I was on my way to Marzetti's, a comfortable restaurant just down the street, where a group of us newspapermen met every morning. We would sit around for an hour drinking coffee, telling stories, drawing pictures on the table-cloth, and giving imitations of the more eminent Ohio political figures of the day, many of whom fanned their soup with their hats but had enough good, old-fashioned horse sense to realise that a proposal to shift the clocks of the state from Central to Eastern standard time was directly contrary to the will of the Lord God Almighty and that the supporters of the project would burn in hell.

After this relaxing and often stimulating interlude I would stroll out to the Carnegie Library and read the New York *World* in the periodical room. It so happened that the city offices, which I was assigned to cover, were housed at that time in the library building, the old City Hall having burned down the first night I ever attended a council meeting in it. After I had put the *World* back on its rack, only a little fragment of forenoon remained in which to gather the news, but I somehow managed the aggravating chore.

Nor were the city offices dull and colourless places. Secretary Killam of the Civil Service Commission had a tuba, on which I learned to play a few notes, an exciting and satisfying experience, as anyone who has brought forth a blast from a tuba knows. The lady dance-hall inspector was full of stories of the goings on in the more dubious clubs about town, in one of which, she reported, the boys and girls contrived the two-step without moving their feet. And the Mayor's office was frequently besieged by diverting and passionate taxpayers: an elderly gentleman who could get KDKA on the steel rims of his spectacles, a woman who was warned of the approach of earthquakes by a sharp twinge in her left side, and a lady to whom it had been revealed in a vision that the new O'Shoughnessy storage dam had not been constructed of concrete but of Cream of Wheat.

So ran the mornings away in the years of my servitude on the Columbus *Dispatch*. The afternoons, after three o'clock, I had to myself. I used to spend a great many of them at home, lying down. That tuba took quite a little out of me.

Now we come to the six months of drudgery on the New York *Evening Post*, back in the days of Sacco and Vanzetti, the Hall-Mills case, and Daddy Browning. The city editor of the paper, a gentleman with a keen eye for the frailties of men and a heart overflowing with *misericordia*, apparently decided I did not look like a man capable of handling spot news – that is, events in the happening, such as warehouse fires and running gun fights. He therefore set me to writing what he called overnight feature stories. These were stories that could be printed anytime – tomorrow, or next week, or not at all, if the flow of important news was too heavy. They were designed to fit in between accounts of murder trials and train wrecks, to brighten the ominous page and lighten, if possible, the uneasy heart of the reader. So it came about that when other reporters were out wearing themselves down in quest of the clangorous and complicated fact, I could be observed wandering the quiet shore above the noisy torrent of contemporary history, examining the little miracles and grotesqueries of the time.

I wrote only one story a day, usually consisting of fewer than a thousand words. Most of the reporters, when they went out on assignments, first had to get their foot in the door, but the portals of the fantastic and the unique are always left open. If an astonished botanist produced a black evening primrose, or thought he had produced one, I spent the morning prowling his gardens. When a lady in the West Seventies sent in word that she was getting messages from the late Walter Savage Landor in heaven, I was sent up to see what the importunate poet had on his mind. On the occasion of the arrival in town of Major Monroe of Jacksonville, Florida, who claimed to be a hundred and seventeen years old, I walked up Broadway with him while he roundly cursed the Northern dogs who jostled him, bewailing the while the passing of Bob Lee and Tom Jackson and Joe Johnston. I studied gypsies in Canarsie and generals in the Waldorf, listened to a man talk backward, and watched a blindfolded boy play ping-pong. Put it all together and I don't know what it comes to, but it wasn't drudgery.

It was not often, in the *Post* or no *Sturm-und-Drang* phase, that I wandered further afield than the confines of Greater New York. On the occasion of the hundred-and-fiftieth anniversary of Washington's crossing the Delaware, however, I was sent over to Trenton to report the daylong celebration. (Once in a long while I got a spot news assignment like that.) At a little past ten in the morning I discovered the hotel room which a group of the more convivial newspapermen had set up as their headquarters, and at a little past twelve I was asleep in a chair there. When I woke up it was dark, and the celebration was over. I hadn't sent anything to my paper, and by that time it was too late. I went home. The *Post*, I found out, had used the Associated Press account of what went on in Trenton.

When I got to work the next morning, the city editor came over to my desk. 'Let's see,' he said, 'what did I send you out on yesterday?' 'It didn't pan out,' I told him. 'No story.' 'The hell with it, then,' he said. 'Here, get on this – lady says there are violets growing in the snow over in Red Bank.' 'Violets don't grow in the snow,' I reminded him. 'They might in Red Bank,' he said. 'Slide on over there.' I slid instead to a bar and put in a phone call to the Chief of Police in Red Bank. A desk sergeant answered and I asked him about the violets. 'Ain't no violence over here,' he told me, and hung up. It wasn't much to hang a story on, as we say, but I hung one on it. But first I had a few more drinks with a man I had met at the bar, very pleasant fellow, captain of a barge or something. Shortly after the strange case of the violets in the snow, I left the newspaper game and drifted into the magazine game.

And now, in closing, I wish to leave with my little readers, both boys and girls, this parting bit of advice: Stay out of the magazine game.

THE CATBIRD SEAT

Mr Martin bought the pack of Camels on Monday night in the most crowded cigar store on Broadway. It was theatre time and seven or eight men were buying cigarettes. The clerk didn't even glance at Mr Martin, who put the pack in his overcoat pocket and went out. If any of the staff at F. & S. had seen him buy the cigarettes, they would have been astonished, for it was generally known that Mr Martin did not smoke, and never had. No one saw him.

It was just a week to the day since Mr Martin had decided to rub out Mrs Ulgine Barrows. The term 'rub out' pleased him because it suggested nothing more than the correction of an error – in this case an error of Mr Fitweiler. Mr Martin had spent each night of the past week working out his plan and examining it. As he walked home now he went over it again. For the hundredth time he resented the element of imprecision, the margin of guesswork that entered into the business. The project as he had worked it out was casual and bold, the risks were considerable. Something might go wrong anywhere along the line. And therein lay the cunning of his scheme. No one would ever see in it the cautious, painstaking hand of Erwin Martin, head of the filing department at F. & S., of whom Mr Fitweiler had once said, 'Man is fallible but Martin isn't.' No one would see his hand, that is, unless it were caught in the act.

Sitting in his apartment, drinking a glass of milk, Mr Martin reviewed his case against Mrs Ulgine Barrows, as he had every night for seven nights. He began at the beginning. Her quacking voice and braying laugh had first profaned the halls of F. & S. on 7 March 1941 (Mr Martin had a head for dates). Old Roberts, the personnel chief, had introduced her as the newly appointed special adviser to the president of the firm, Mr Fitweiler. The woman had appalled Mr Martin instantly, but he hadn't shown it. He had given her his dry hand, a look of studious concentration, and a faint smile. 'Well,' she had said, looking at the papers on his desk, 'are you lifting the oxcart out of the ditch?' As Mr Martin recalled that moment, over his milk, he squirmed slightly. He must keep his mind on her crimes as a special adviser, not on her peccadillos as a personality. This he found difficult to do, in spite of entering an objection and sustaining it. The faults of the woman as a woman kept chattering on in his mind like an unruly witness. She had, for almost two years now, baited him. In the halls, in the elevator, even in his own office, into which she romped now and then like a circus horse, she was constantly shouting these silly questions at him. 'Are you lifting the oxcart out of the ditch? Are you tearing up the pea patch? Are you hollering down the rain barrel? Are you scraping around the bottom of the pickle barrel? Are you sitting in the catbird seat?'

It was Joey Hart, one of Mr Martin's two assistants, who had explained what the gibberish meant. 'She must be a Dodger fan,' he had said. 'Red Barber announces the Dodger games over the radio and he uses those expressions – picked 'em up down South.' Joey had gone on to explain one or two. 'Tearing up the pea patch' meant going on a rampage; 'sitting in the catbird seat' meant sitting pretty, like a batter with three balls and no strikes on him. Mr Martin dismissed all this with an effort. It had been annoying, it had driven him near to distraction, but he was too solid a man to be moved to murder by anything so childish. It was fortunate, he reflected as he passed on to the important charges against Mrs Barrows, that he had stood up under it so well. He had maintained always an outward appearance of polite tolerance. 'Why, I even believe you like the woman,' Miss Paird, his other assistant, had once said to him. He had simply smiled.

A gavel rapped in Mr Martin's mind and the case proper was resumed. Mrs Ulgine Barrows stood charged with wilful, blatant and persistent attempts to destroy the efficiency and system of F. & S. It was competent, material and relevant to review her advent and rise to power. Mr Martin had got the story from Miss Paird, who seemed always able to find things out. According to her, Mrs Barrows had met Mr Fitweiler at a party, where she had rescued him from the embraces of a powerfully built drunken man who had mistaken the president of F. & S. for a famous retired Middle Western football coach. She had led him to a sofa and somehow worked upon him a monstrous magic. The aging gentleman had jumped to the conclusion there and then that this was a woman of singular attainments, equipped to bring out the best in him and in the firm. A week later he had introduced her into F. & S. as his special adviser. On that day confusion got its foot in the door. After Miss Tyson, Mr Brundage and Mr Bartlett had been fired and Mr Munson had taken his hat and stalked out, mailing in his resignation later, old Roberts had been emboldened to speak to Mr Fitweiler. He mentioned that Mr Munson's department had been 'a little disrupted' and hadn't they perhaps better resume the old system there? Mr Fitweiler had said certainly not. He had the greatest faith in Mrs Barrow's ideas. 'They require a little seasoning, a little seasoning, is all,' he had added. Mr Roberts had given it up. Mr Martin reviewed in detail all the changes wrought by Mrs Barrows. She had begun chipping at the cornices of the firm's edifice and now she was swinging at the foundation stones with a pickaxe.

Mr Martin came now, in his summing up, to the afternoon of Monday, 2 November 1942 – just one week ago. On that day, at 3 p.m., Mrs Barrows had bounced into his office. 'Boo!' she had yelled. 'Are you scraping around the bottom of the pickle barrel?' Mr Martin had looked at her from under his green eyeshade, saying nothing. She had begun to wander about the office, taking it in with her great, popping eyes. 'Do you really need *all* these filing cabinets?' she had demanded suddenly. Mr Martin's heart had jumped. 'Each of these files', he had said, keeping his voice even, 'plays an indispensable part in the system of F. & S.' She had brayed at him, 'Well, don't tear up the pea patch!' and gone to the door. From there she had bawled, 'But you sure have got a lot of fine scrap in here!' Mr Martin could no longer doubt that the finger was on his beloved department. Her pickaxe was on the upswing, poised for the first blow. It had not come yet; he had received no blue memo from the enchanted Mr Fitweiler bearing nonsensical instructions deriving from the obscene woman. But there was no doubt in Mr Martin's mind that one would be forthcoming. He must act quickly. Already a precious week had gone by. Mr Martin stood up in his living-room, still holding his milk glass. 'Gentlemen of the jury,' he said to himself, 'I demand the death penalty for this horrible person.'

The next day Mr Martin followed his routine, as usual. He polished his glasses more often and once sharpened an already sharp pencil, but not even Miss Paird noticed. Only once did he catch sight of his victim; she swept past him in the hall with a patronising 'Hi!' At five-thirty he walked home, as usual, and had a glass of milk, as usual. He had never drunk anything stronger in his life – unless you could count ginger ale. The late Sam Schlosser, the S. of F. & S., had praised Mr Martin at a staff meeting several years before for his temperate habits. 'Our most efficient worker neither drinks nor smokes,' he had said. 'The results speak for themselves.' Mr Fitweiler had sat by, nodding approval.

Mr Martin was still thinking about that red-letter day as he walked over to the Schrafft's on Fifth Avenue near Forty-sixth Street. He got there, as he always did, at eight o'clock. He finished his dinner and the financial page of the *Sun* at a quarter to nine, as he always did. It was his custom after dinner to take a walk. This time he walked down Fifth Avenue at a casual pace. His gloved hands felt moist and warm, his forehead cold. He transferred the Camels from his overcoat to a jacket pocket. He wondered, as he did so, if they did not represent an unnecessary note of strain. Mrs Barrows smoked only Luckies. It was his idea to puff a few puffs on a Camel (after the rubbing-out), stub it out in the ashtray holding her lipstick-stained Luckies, and thus drag a small red herring across the trail. Perhaps it was not a good idea. It would take time. He might even choke, too loudly.

Mr Martin had never seen the house on West Twelfth Street where Mrs Barrows lived, but he had a clear enough picture of it. Fortunately, she had bragged to everybody about her ducky first-floor apartment in the perfectly darling three-storey redbrick. There would be no doorman or other attendants; just the tenants of the second and third floors. As he walked along, Mr Martin realised that he would get there before nine-thirty. He had considered walking north on Fifth Avenue from Schrafft's to a point from which it would take him until ten o'clock to reach the house. At that hour people were less likely to be coming in or going out. But the procedure would have made an awkward loop in the straight thread of his casualness, and he had abandoned it. It was impossible to figure when people would be entering or leaving the house, anyway. There was a great risk at any hour. If he ran into anybody, he would simply have to place the rubbing-out of Ulgine Barrows in the inactive file forever. The same thing would hold true if there were someone in her apartment. In that case he would just say that he had been passing by, recognised her charming house and thought to drop in.

It was eighteen minutes after nine when Mr Martin turned into Twelfth Street. A man passed him, and a man and a woman talking. There was no one within fifty paces when he came to the house, half-way down the block. He was up the steps and in the small vestibule in no time, pressing the bell under the card that said 'Mrs Ulgine Barrows'. When the clicking in the lock started, he jumped forward against the door. He got inside fast, closing the door behind him. A bulb in a lantern hung from the hall ceiling on a chain seemed to give a monstrously bright light. There was nobody on the stairs, which went up ahead of him along the left wall. A door opened down the hall in the wall on the right. He went toward it swiftly, on tiptoe.

'Well, for God's sake, look who's here!' bawled Mrs Barrows, and her braying laugh rang out like a report of a shotgun. He rushed past her like a football tackle, bumping her. 'Hey, quit shoving!' she said, closing the door behind them. They were in her living-room, which seemed to Mr Martin to be lighted by a hundred lamps. 'What's after you?' she said. 'You're as jumpy as a goat.' He found he was unable to speak. His heart was wheezing in his throat. 'I – yes,' he finally brought out. She was jabbering and laughing as she started to help him off with his coat. 'No, no,' he said. 'I'll put it here.' He took it off and put it on a chair near the door. 'Your hat and gloves, too,' she said. 'You're in a lady's house.' He put his hat on top of the coat. Mrs Barrows seemed larger than he had thought. He kept his gloves on. 'I was passing by,' he said. 'I recognised – is there anyone here?' She laughed louder than ever. 'No', she said, 'we're all alone. You're as white as a sheet, you funny man. Whatever *has* come over you? I'll mix you a toddy.' She started toward a door across the room. 'Scotch-and-soda be all right? But say, you don't drink, do you?' She turned and gave him her amused look. Mr Martin pulled himself together. 'Scotch-and-soda will be all right,' he heard himself say. He could hear her laughing in the kitchen.

Mr Martin looked quickly around the living-room for the weapon. He had counted on finding one there. There were handirons and a poker and something in a corner that looked like an Indian club. None of them would do. It couldn't be that way. He began to pace around. He came to a desk. On it lay a metal paper knife with an ornate handle. Would it be sharp enough? He reached for it and knocked over a small brass jar. Stamps spilled out of it and it fell to the floor with a clatter. 'Hey,' Mrs Barrows yelled from the kitchen, 'are you tearing up the pea patch?' Mr Martin gave a strange laugh. Picking up the knife, he tried its point against his left wrist. It was blunt. It wouldn't do.

When Mrs Barrows reappeared, carrying two highballs, Mr Martin, standing there with his gloves on, became acutely conscious of the fantasy he had wrought. Cigarettes in his pocket, a drink prepared for him – it was all too grossly improbable. It was more than that; it was impossible. Somewhere in the back of his mind a vague idea stirred, sprouted. 'For heaven's sake, take off those gloves,' said Mrs Barrows. 'I always wear them in the house,' said Mr Martin. The idea began to bloom, strange and wonderful. She put the glasses on a coffee table in front of a sofa and sat on the sofa. 'Come over here, you odd little man,' she said. Mr Martin went over and sat beside her. It was difficult getting a cigarette out of the pack of Camels, but he managed it. She held a match for him, laughing. 'Well,' she said, handing him his drink, 'this is perfectly marvellous. You with a drink and a cigarette.'

Mr Martin puffed, not too awkwardly, and took a gulp of the highball. 'I drink and smoke all the time,' he said. He clinked his glass against hers. 'Here's nuts to that old windbag, Fitweiler,' he said, and gulped again. The stuff tasted awful, but he made no grimace. 'Really, Mr Martin,' she said, her voice and posture changing, 'you are insulting our employer.' Mrs Barrows was now all special adviser to the president. 'I am preparing a bomb', said Mr Martin, 'which will blow the old goat higher than hell.' He had only had a little of the drink, which was not strong. It couldn't be that. 'Do you take dope or something?' Mrs Barrows asked coldly. 'Heroin,' said Mr Martin. 'I'll be coked to the gills when I bump that old buzzard off.' 'Mr Martin!' she shouted, getting to her feet. 'That will be all of that. You must go at once.' Mr Martin took another swallow of his drink. He tapped his cigarette out in the ashtray and put the pack of Camels on the coffee table. Then he got up. She stood glaring at him. He walked over and put on his hat and coat. 'Not a word about this,' he said, and laid an index finger against his lips. All Mrs Barrows could bring out was 'Really!' Mr Martin put his hand on the doorknob. 'I'm sitting in the catbird seat,' he said. He stuck his tongue out at her and left. Nobody saw him go.

Mr Martin got to his apartment, walking, well before eleven. No one saw him go in. He had two glasses of milk after brushing his teeth, and he felt elated. It wasn't tipsiness, because he hadn't been tipsy. Anyway, the walk had worn off all effects of the whisky. He got in bed and read a magazine for a while. He was asleep before midnight.

Mr Martin got to the office at eight-thirty the next morning, as usual. At a quarter to nine, Ulgine Barrows, who had never before arrived at work before ten, swept into his office. 'I'm reporting to Mr Fitweiler now!' she shouted. 'If he turns you over to the police, it's no more than you deserve!' Mr Martin gave her a look of shocked surprise. 'I beg your pardon?' he said. Mrs Barrows snorted and bounced out of the room, leaving Miss Paird and Joey Hart staring after her. 'What's the matter with that old devil now?' asked Miss Paird. 'I have no idea,' said Mr Martin, resuming his work. The other two looked at him and then at each other. Miss Paird got up and went out. She walked slowly past the closed door of Mr Fitweiler's office. Mrs Barrows was yelling inside, but she was not braying. Miss Paird could not hear what the woman was saying. She went back to her desk.

Forty-five minutes later, Mrs Barrows left the president's office and went into her own, shutting the door. It wasn't until half an hour later that Mr Fitweiler sent for Mr Martin. The head of the filing department, neat, quiet, attentive, stood in front of the old man's desk. Mr Fitweiler was pale and nervous. He took his glasses off and twiddled them. He made a small, bruffing sound in his throat. 'Martin,' he said, 'you have been with us more than twenty years.' 'Twenty-two, sir,' said Mr Martin. 'In that time,' pursued the president, 'your work and your – uh – manner have been exemplary.' 'I trust so, sir,' said Mr Martin. 'I have understood, Martin,' said Mr Fitweiler, 'that you have never taken a drink or smoked.' 'That is correct, sir,' said Mr Martin. 'Ah, yes.' Mr Fitweiler polished his glasses. 'You may describe what you did after leaving the office yesterday, Martin,' he said. Mr Martin allowed less than a second for his bewildered pause. 'Certainly, sir,' he said. 'I walked home. Then I went to Schrafft's for dinner. Afterward I walked home again. I went to bed early, sir, and read a magazine for a while. I was asleep before eleven.' 'Ah, yes,' said Mr Fitweiler again. He was silent for a moment, searching for the proper words to say to the head of the filing department. 'Mrs Barrows,' he said finally, 'Mrs Barrows has worked hard, Martin, very hard. It grieves me to report that she has suffered a severe breakdown. It has taken the form of a persecution complex accompanied by distressing hallucinations.' 'I am very sorry, sir,' said Mr Martin. 'Mrs Barrows is under the delusion', continued Mr Fitweiler, 'that you visited her last evening and behaved yourself in an – uh – unseemly manner.' He raised his hand to silence Mr Martin's little pained outcry. 'It is the nature of these psychological diseases', Mr Fitweiler said, 'to fix upon the least likely and most innocent party as the – uh – source of persecution. These matters are not for the lay mind to grasp, Martin. I've just had my psychiatrist, Dr Fitch, on the phone. He would not, of course, commit himself, but he made enough generalisations to substantiate my suspicions. I suggested to Mrs Barrows when she had completed her – uh – story to me this morning, that she visit Dr Fitch, for I suspected a condition at once. She flew, I regret to say, into a rage, and demanded – uh – requested that I call you on the carpet. You may not know, Martin, but Mrs Barrows had planned a reorganisation of your department – subject to my approval, of course, subject to my approval. This brought you, rather than anyone else, to her mind – but again that is a phenomenon for Dr Fitch and not for us. So, Martin, I am afraid Mrs Barrows' usefulness here is at an end.' 'I am dreadfully sorry, sir,' said Mr Martin.

It was at this point that the door to the office blew open with the suddenness of a gas-main explosion and Mrs Barrows catapulted through it. 'Is the little rat denying it?' she screamed. 'He can't get away with that!' Mr Martin got up and moved discreetly to a point beside Mr Fitweiler's chair. 'You drank and smoked at my apartment,' she bawled at Mr Martin, 'and you know it! You called Mr Fitweiler an old windbag and said you were going to blow him up when you got coked to the gills on your heroin!' She stopped yelling to catch her breath and a new glint came into her popping eyes. 'If you weren't such a drab, ordinary little man,' she said, 'I'd think you'd planned it all. Sticking your tongue out, saying you were sitting in the catbird seat, because you thought no one would believe me when I told it! My God, it's really too perfect!' She brayed loudly and hysterically, and the fury was on her again. She glared at Mr Fitweiler. 'Can't you see how he has tricked us, you old fool? Can't you see his little game?' But Mr Fitweiler had been surreptitiously pressing all the buttons under the top of his desk and employees of F. & S. began pouring into the room. 'Stockton,' said Mr Fitweiler, 'you and Fishbein will take Mrs Barrows to her home. Mrs Powell, you will go with them.' Stockton, who had played a little football in high school, blocked Mrs Barrows as she made for Mr Martin. It took him and Fishbein together to force her out of the door into the hall, crowded with stenographers and office boys. She was still screaming imprecations at Mr Martin, tangled and contradictory imprecations. The hubbub finally died out down the corridor.

'I regret that this has happened,' said Mr Fitweiler. 'I shall ask you to dismiss it from your mind, Martin.' 'Yes, sir,' said Mr Martin, anticipating his chief's 'That will be all' by moving to the door. 'I will dismiss it.' He went out and shut the door, and his step was light and quick in the hall. When he entered his department he had slowed down to his customary gait, and he walked quietly across the room to the W20 file, wearing a look of studious concentration.

THE LADY ON THE BOOKCASE

One day twelve years ago an outraged cartoonist, four of whose drawings had been rejected in a clump by *The New Yorker*, stormed into the office of Harold Ross, editor of the magazine. 'Why is it', demanded the cartoonist, 'that you reject my work and publish drawings by a fifth-rate artist like Thurber?' Ross came quickly to my defence like the true friend and devoted employer he is. 'You mean third-rate,' he said quietly, but there was a warning glint in his steady grey eyes that caused the discomfited cartoonist to beat a hasty retreat.

With the exception of Ross, the interest of editors in what I draw has been rather more journalistic than critical. They want to know if it is true that I draw by moonlight, or under water, and when I say no, they lose interest until they hear the rumour that I found the drawings in an old trunk or that I do the captions while my nephew makes the sketches.

The other day I was shoving some of my originals around on the floor (I do not draw on the floor; I was just shoving the originals around) and they fell, or perhaps I pushed them, into five separate and indistinct categories. I have never wanted to write about my drawings, and I still don't want to, but it

'With you I have known peace, Lida, and now you say you're going crazy.'

occurred to me that it might be a good idea to do it now, when everybody is busy with something else, and get it over quietly.

Category No. 1, then, which may be called the Unconscious or Stream of Nervousness category, is represented by 'With you I have known peace, Lida, and now you say you're going crazy' and the drawing entitled with simple dignity, 'Home'. These drawings were done while the artist was thinking of something else (or so he has been assured by experts) and hence his hand was guided by the Unconscious which, in turn, was more or less influenced by the Subconscious.

Home

Students of Jung have instructed me that Lida and the House-Woman are representations of the *anima*, the female essence or directive which floats around in the ageless universal Subconscious of Man like a tadpole in a cistern. Less intellectual critics insist that the two ladies are actual persons I have consciously known. Between these two schools of thought lies a discouragingly large space of time extending roughly from 1,000,000 BC to the middle nineteen-thirties.

Whenever I try to trace the true identity of the House-

Woman, I get to thinking of Mr Jones. He appeared in my office one day twelve years ago, said he was Mr Jones, and asked me to lend him 'Home' for reproduction in an art-magazine. I never saw the drawing again. Tall, well-dressed, kind of sad-looking chap, and as well spoken a gentleman as you would want to meet.

Category No. 2 brings us to Freud and another one of those discouragingly large spaces – namely, the space between the Concept of the Purely Accidental and the Theory of Haphazard Determination. Whether chance is capricious or we are all prisoners of pattern is too long and cloudy a subject to go into here. I shall consider each of the drawings in Category No. 2, explaining what happened and leaving the definition of the forces involved up to you. The seal on top of the bed, then ('All right, have it your way – you heard a seal bark'), started out to be a seal on a rock. The rock, in the process of being drawn, began to look like the head of a bed, so I made a bed out of it, put a man and wife in the bed, and stumbled on to the caption as easily and unexpectedly as the seal had stumbled into the bedroom.

'All right, have it your way – you heard a seal bark.'

'That's my first wife up there, and this is the present Mrs Harris.'

The woman on top of the bookcase ('That's my first wife up there, and this is the *present* Mrs Harris') was originally designed to be a woman crouched on the top step of a staircase, but since the tricks and conventions of perspective and planes sometimes fail me, the staircase assumed the shape of a bookcase and was finished as such, to the surprise and embarrassment of the first Mrs Harris, the present Mrs Harris, the visitor, Mr Harris, and me. Before *The New Yorker* would print the drawing, they phoned me long distance to inquire whether the first Mrs Harris was alive or dead or stuffed. I replied that my taxidermist had advised me that you cannot stuff a woman, and that my physician had informed me that a dead lady cannot support herself on all fours. This meant, I said, that the first Mrs Harris was unquestionably alive.

The man riding on the other man's shoulders in the bar ('For the last time, you and your horsie get away from me and stay away!') was intended to be standing alongside the irate speaker, but I started his head up too high and made it too small, so that he would have been nine feet tall if I had completed his body that way. It was but the work of thirty-two seconds to put him on another man's shoulders. As simple or, if

'For the last time, you and your horsie get away from me and stay away!'

you like, as complicated as that. The psychological factors which may be present here are, as I have indicated, elaborate and confused. Personally, I like Dr Claude Thornway's theory of the Deliberate Accident or Conditioned Mistake.

Category No. 3 is perhaps a variant of Category No. 2; indeed, they may even be identical. The dogs in 'The father

'The father belonged to some people who were driving through in a Packard.'

belonged to some people who were driving through in a Packard' were drawn as a captionless spot, and the interior with figures just sort of grew up around them. The hippopotamus in 'What have you done with Dr Millmoss?' was drawn to amuse my small daughter. Something about the creature's expression when he was completed convinced me that he had recently eaten a man. I added the hat and pipe and Mrs Millmoss, and the caption followed easily enough. Incidentally, my daughter, who was two years old at the time, identified the beast immediately. 'That's a hippotomanus,' she said. *The New Yorker* was not so smart. They described the drawing for their files as follows: 'Woman with strange animal'. *The New Yorker* was nine years old at the time.

'*What have you done with Dr Millmoss?*'

Category No. 4 is represented by perhaps the best known of some fifteen drawings belonging to this special grouping, which may be called the Contributed Idea Category. This drawing ('Touché!') was originally done for *The New Yorker* by Carl Rose, caption and all. Mr Rose is a realistic artist, and his gory scene distressed the editors, who hate violence. They asked Rose if he would let me have the idea, since there is obviously no blood to speak of in the people I draw. Rose graciously

'Touché!'

consented. No one who looks at 'Touché!' believes that the man whose head is in the air is really dead. His opponent will hand it back to him with profuse apologies, and the discommoded fencer will replace it on his shoulders and say, 'No harm done, forget it.' Thus the old controversy as to whether death can be made funny is left just where it was before Carl Rose came along with his wonderful idea.

Category No. 5, our final one, can be called, believe it or not, the Intentional or Thought-Up Category. The idea for each of these two drawings just came to me and I sat down and made a

'Well, I'm disenchanted, too. We're all disenchanted.'

sketch to fit the prepared caption. Perhaps, in the case of 'Well, I'm disenchanted, too. We're all disenchanted,' another one of those Outside Forces played a part. That is, I may have over-heard a husband say to his wife, on the street or at a party, 'I'm disenchanted.' I do not think this is true, however, in the case of the rabbit-headed doctor and his woman patient. I believe that scene and its caption came to me one night in bed. I *may* have got the idea in a doctor's office or a rabbit hutch, but I don't think so.

'You said a moment ago that everybody you look at seems to be a rabbit. Now just what do you mean by that, Mrs Sprague?'

If you want to, you can cut these drawings out and push them around on the floor, making your own categories or applying your own psychological theories; or you can even invent some fresh rumours. I should think it would be more fun, though, to take a nap, or baste a roast, or run around the reservoir in Central Park.

A GUIDE TO THE LITERARY PILGRIMAGE

In a certain restaurant on Third Avenue, whose proprietors are patrons of the arts, I was standing at the bar one evening, smiling in my beer, when a short, bald, middle-aged man appeared at my shoulder and said, 'What sets *you* off from the other temperaments in this ateleer, Mac?' I could have run the fellow through with that cold, steady stare of mine which has been called 'brown ice', but I found, a little to my surprise, that I had an answer to his question. 'I am the only living writer', I said, 'who has not called on George Bernard Shaw and who does not want to call on George Bernard Shaw.' The character at my shoulder, who had expected to call forth from me a foolish grin and a few stammered words, slunk sheepishly down the bar to insult a rather peaked etcher who was quietly cursing to himself. I was left to examine, the way a squirrel examines a nut, the sudden little definition of singularity which I had tossed off. I could find no flaws in it.

It is not that I have anything against George Bernard Shaw or fail to appreciate his genius. It is neither an emotional blockage nor a mental judgement which stands in the way of my wanting to call on him. It is, I think, a purely nervous apprehension. I am afraid, perhaps, that I would sit in the great man's study gaping like a badly carved jack-o'-lantern, squirming and stammering like the hobbledehoy I really am under my well-groomed exterior, behind my mask of cold indifference.

On top of this singularly personal attitude toward calling on Shaw, there had been superimposed a pattern of actual experience – not my own experience, to be sure, but that of two other writers, Ralph Waldo Emerson and a man whom I shall call Mitchell Morris. The adventures of these two gentlemen in the homes of the literary great have persuaded me of a basic and unfortunate fact about the literary pilgrimage: it almost never comes off very well.

Emerson may have founded the American cult of the literary pilgrimage; at any rate, he risked a tricky stomach on a sailing ship more than a hundred years ago to pay his respects to Wordsworth, Coleridge, Carlyle, and Landor. He found in Carlyle a man who was to become a lifelong friend (they even kind of romped together, a thing I would have gone a long way to see), but he didn't do so well with the others. Wordsworth, who had just broken a front tooth, recited two sonnets while he and his guest both stood looking at each other – surely one of the most uncomfortable moments in the annals of the literary pilgrimage. Coleridge wore green spectacles and argued querulously about Unitarianism. Landor disagreed about almost everything his visitor brought up, from military leaders through Southey to the Latin poets.

The case of my writer friend, Mitchell Morris, was more recent and quite different. Morris called on the late William Bolitho at his villa in southern France about fifteen years ago. After my friend had presented himself, Bolitho said, 'I will talk for an hour and you will talk for an hour.'

The Bolitho system of literary communion has never seemed sound to me. If I were the man told off to speak last, I would not be able to take in what the other man was saying because I would be trying to think of something to say when my own turn came. This would lead to the stiff posture, the horrible smile, the inattentive monosyllabic interjection, and the glazed expression of the eye. When my host's hour was up, I am afraid I would only be able to repeat, over and over, 'This is a mighty nice place you've got here.'

If the adventures of Emerson and Morris in the living-rooms of the great serve to prove that the literary communion of literary men is by no means a pleasurable and relaxing way to pass an afternoon, the experience of another writer I know who called on André Gide in North Africa recently establishes the rare and pleasant exception to the rule. The distinguished old Frenchman, it came out, was, at the moment, immersed in a profound study of the works of the American intellectual, Dashiell Hammett. Now, the works of Dashiell Hammett happen to constitute a field in which I can hold my own with anyone, a field in which, on one occasion, I even held my own with the celebrated author himself.

I should explain, at this point, that Mr Hammett and I did

not meet by appointment. He did not call on me and I did not call on him. We ran into each other at Tony's, once the fashionable meeting place of the literati of two continents. In Tony's in the old days, literary communion was informal to the point of rough-and-tumble, and a writer did not sit at the feet of another writer unless he was knocked there.

Well (to get further and further away from my friend's call on Gide), Hammett was pleased to announce that the only author whose writing had influenced his own was the late Henry James. It chanced that the subtle but notable similarities between *The Maltese Falcon* and *The Wings of the Dove* had been apparent to me long before they were exposed by Henry Morton Robinson. My own monograph on this curious literary resemblance, *Could Dashiell Hammett Have Created Sam Spade and Ned Beaumont if Henry James Had Not Created Merton Densher and Lambert Strether?*, had, unfortunately, been stored in a warehouse in Bridgeport which burned down in 1934.

Furthermore, it would be just my luck, if I called on Gide, to catch him during a period of Hammett-fag, so that he would be in no mood to listen to the brilliant and carefully prepared parallel I can draw between *The Glass Key* and *The Golden Bowl*. Monsieur Gide would probably open up on me by saying, 'You are familiar, of course, with the works of Aristide Luchon?' It is my embarrassed tendency in such cases to reply, 'Yes. Oh, yes, indeed.' Surely no one can imagine a more awful way to spend an afternoon than by attempting to discuss novels or plays one has never read, written by a man one has never heard of.

My fear about Shaw is that he might, to get back at me for some casual mention of the resemblance between *The Thin Man* and *The Sacred Fount, invent* out of thin air a writer named Aristide Luchon. In all the calendar of dirty tricks one writer can play on another, this is the dirtiest. I believe that Shaw would be capable of such black devilry. In fact, I sometimes see him, in my dreams, leaning towards me and saying, 'Do you agree with me that the character of Mathilde in Luchon's *Dormir Avant le Coucher du Soleil* is badly thought out?' I ride into that with all the reckless courage of Senator Bricker, crying, 'I do, indeed!' and the fat is in the fire, the cat out of the bag, the jig up, and my audience with Shaw at an end. His satanic laughter, as I run full upon his rapier, rings through my nightmares and brings me, panting and terrified, awake.

These nightmares inspired me to work on a set of rules called *The Young Writer's Guide to the Literary Pilgrimage*. The rules are by no means complete, but if they serve to lighten in any way the burden of the visiting – or of the visited – author, I shall be amply repaid for my pains.

RULE I. Bear in mind always that you are the minor artist and that the man you are calling on is the major artist. Otherwise, he would be calling on you. He is not going to write an article about your visit to him; hence, who you are and what you have written will serve only to embarrass him. Thus, it is extremely bad form to present yourself with a loud, proud 'I am George Benton Fields.' The great man might respond with a pseudo-hearty 'Well, I should say you are!' * and the interview would be off to an awkward start. It is equally unfortunate and dangerous to open up with a muttered 'My name is Fields, sir.' Your host might bellow irritably, 'Speak up, man!', or he might address you all afternoon as Mr Fieldser, which would be most uncomfortable.

Sedulously avoid any of the three principal forms of the General or Indefinite Introduction. These are as follows: 1. The Modest or Casual Presentation: 'I am a writer from Seattle, Washington.' 2. The Self-Derogatory Introduction: 'I am a broken-hearted bum from Warren, Ohio.' 3. The Flippant or Facetious Identification: 'I am a little stiff from Bowling Green, and my actuary gives me only thirty-five years to live.' In the first place, you will have made an appointment (if not, you might as well get back on your bicycle), so the Master will know who you are and what you want, in a general sort of way. Just say 'How do you do, sir?' and let him take the lead from there.

RULE II. Do not attempt to impress the great man with some observation or aphorism of your own which you have carefully polished up for the occasion, such as 'The noblest study of mankind is insects,' or 'The César Franck D Minor Symphony is a fraternity whistle,' or 'Clover leaves rarely strike four times in the same place,' or 'There are two ways to get a subject down – pat and mike.' The ice may never be broken if you start out like that.

*A comeback made by the late Clare Briggs when a total stranger approached him with 'I am Henry Preston Barnes.'

RULE III. Do not come out with (and this is especially directed to the visiting female author) 'I have simply *devoured every* line you have ever written, and I *adore* them all!' If, by the end of the afternoon (or of the first five minutes), the great man comes to the conclusion that you are an undiscriminating ass, he may be moved to do some rash and deplorable violence to his novels or plays. Many a distinguished author in his advanced years has completely revised the entire body of his work, usually for the worse. The reason has long remained a mystery, but in the lady who devours and adores every line, I think we have the answer.

RULE IV. Keep all critics' names out of the conversation. Do not say, 'As Van Wyck Brooks [or Bernard De Voto] so aptly put it . . .' It is more than likely that the mention of the name of any critic since Sainte-Beuve has been strictly forbidden in the shrine for more than forty years.

RULE V. Be careful, if you mention any of the writer's works (and you better had), not to confuse him with some other writer. H. G. Wells once said that most of the people who visited him informed him that his best novel by far was *The Old Wives' Tale*.

RULE VI. For God's sake don't recite anything. What do you suppose Wordsworth would have thought if Emerson had recited a couple of his own poems to *him* (Wordsworth)?

RULE VII. Don't bring the celebrated artist a letter of introduction from Herbert Bayard Swope, Clarence Budington Kelland, Robert Alphonso Taft, Gene Tunney, George Palmer Putnam, H. V. Kaltenborn, Dan Golenpaul, or some Scarsdale woman who claims she met the old boy on a ship during a frightful crossing to Pernambuco. It is better not even to mention this woman's name or the name of the ship (or Pernambuco or Scarsdale).

RULE VIII. Do not come into the Presence bearing gifts. He has almost everything, doesn't need anything, and likes practically nothing. Furthermore, it is very hard for him to say 'Thank you'. In the case of a great many offerings, I don't blame him. Here is a list of gifts which should especially be excluded: a clipping of an article written by the eminent gentleman for a school paper when he was fifteen; a copy of one of his plays done on the head of a tenpenny nail; a copy of one of his plays translated into Shawnee by an employee of the Department of the Interior; a paragraph laboriously constructed by rearranging all the words in the titles of all his books and intended to supply a key to What He Has Been Trying to Say; any caricatures, effigies, or likenesses of the great man, particularly those made out of typewriter punctuation marks, embroidery floss, field-corn kernels, buckeyes, matches, toothpicks, pipe cleaners, paper clips, tiddlywinks, dice, pigeon feathers, spools, milk-bottle caps, cigar bands, B B shot, or potatoes. The value of these objects is not enhanced by the fact that they were made by a child under seven, a woman over ninety, a Camp Fire Girl, Mayor O'Dwyer, the seventh daughter of a seventh daughter, or a midget.

RULE IX. Do not take with you your friends and neighbours, Mr and Mrs Howard M. Phillips, who happen to be travelling with you. If I know Mrs Phillips, and I think I do, she will tell about her niece who, though only nine, writes verse and composes music. She will try to read some of the poems, which she always carries in her handbag, and, if there is a piano, she may even play one of the child's sonatas.

RULE X. If, on your arrival, the door is opened by a member of the literary figure's household who says that the Master will not be able to see you for forty-eight hours, do not hang around the house or the neighbourhood. Go away.

RULE XI. If, in such a case, you do go away, do not leave behind, for the distinguished writer to read, a thousand-word note written in longhand and beginning, 'In 1908, when my brother-in-law was an oiler on a Danish cattle boat, he found one of your', etc., etc., etc. Don't leave any note at all. Just go away.

RULE XII. And stay away.

If you are protesting that my Guide to the Literary Pilgrimage does not so much present my reasons for not wanting to call on Shaw as it does his probable reasons for not wanting me, or you (or your Aunt Clara, who once had a piece in Harper's 'Lion's Mouth'), to call on him, I can only point out that my reluctance to make the pilgrimage is implicit in the very nature of the rules. Beyond the suggestion that the visitor should begin with a simple 'How do you do, sir?' the rules do not offer any instructions as to what to say. This is because I have not been able to think of anything to say in the presence of George Bernard Shaw, and I do not believe that Shaw would be amused by anyone who just sat there and said nothing.

The only famous writer I have ever heard of who did not expect his companion to say anything at all was the late Hendrik Willem van Loon. A friend of mine, who used to ride with van Loon from Stamford to New York several times a week, determined one day on a test. He decided to greet van Loon on the Stamford platform on this particular morning simply with a smile and a handshake and to leave him in Grand Central station the same way, having said no word. He wondered if the great man would catch on to the fact that his companion had not once opened his mouth. The next morning, he again came up to van Loon on the Stamford platform and said, 'That was a fine discussion we had on the train yesterday.' 'It was, indeed,' said van Loon. 'I enjoyed it a great deal.'

That would surely be too much to expect of Mr Shaw. Or perhaps I should say too much for Mr Shaw to expect of me. In any event, I have written enough about what I do not intend to say on a literary pilgrimage I am never going to make.

FILE AND FORGET

I want to thank my secretary, Miss Ellen Bagley, for putting the following letters in order. I was not up to the task myself, for reasons that will, I think, become clear to the reader.

J.T.

WEST CORNWALL, CONN.
2 November 1949

Miss Alma Winege,
The Charteriss Publishing Co.,
132 East What Street,
New York, N.Y.

Dear Miss Winege,
    Your letter of October 25th, which you sent to me in care of The Homestead, Hot Springs, Ark., has been forwarded to my home in West Cornwall, Conn., by The Homestead, Hot

Springs, Va. As you know, Mrs Thurber and I sometimes visit this Virginia resort, but we haven't been there for more than a year. Your company, in the great tradition of publishers, has sent so many letters to me at Hot Springs, Ark., that the postmaster there has simply taken to sending them on to the right address, or what would be the right address if I were there. I explained to Mr Cluffman, and also to Miss Lexy, when I last called at your offices, that all mail was to be sent to me at West Cornwall until further notice. If and when I go to The Homestead, I will let you know in advance. Meanwhile, I suggest that you remove from your files all addresses of mine except the West Cornwall one. Another publishing firm recently sent a letter to me at 65 West 11th Street, an address I vacated in the summer of 1930. It would not come as a surprise to me if your firm, or some other publishers, wrote me in care of my mother at 568 Oak Street, Columbus, Ohio. I was thirteen years old when we lived there, back in 1908.

As for the contents of your letter of the 25th, I did not order thirty-six copies of Peggy Peckham's book, *Grandma Was a Nudist*. I trust that you have not shipped these books to me in care of The Homestead, Hot Springs, Ark., or anywhere else.

Sincerely yours,

J. THURBER

PS. Margaret Peckham, by the way, is not the author of this book. She is the distinguished New York psychiatrist whose *The Implications of Nudism* was published a couple of years ago. She never calls herself Peggy.

J.T.

WEST CORNWALL, CONN.

3 November 1949

Miss Alma Winege,
The Charteriss Publishing Co.,
New York, N.Y.

Dear Miss Winege,

In this morning's mail I received a card from the Grand Central branch of the New York Post Office informing me that a package of books had been delivered to me at 410 East 57th

Street. The branch office is holding the package for further postage, which runs to a considerable amount. I am enclosing the notification card, since these must be the thirty-six copies of *Grandma was a Nudist*. I have not lived at 410 East 57th Street since the fall of 1944. Please see to it that this address is removed from your files, along with The Homestead address.

Whoever ordered those books, if anyone actually did, probably wonders where they are.

Sincerely yours,

J. THURBER

THE CHARTERISS PUBLISHING COMPANY
NEW YORK, N.Y.

5 November 1949

Mr James M. Thurber,
West Cornwall, Conn.

Dear Mr Thurber,

I am dreadfully sorry about the mix-up over Miss Peckham's book. We have been pretty much upset around here since the departure of Mr Peterson and Mr West, and several new girls came to us with the advent of Mr Jordan. They have not yet got their 'sea legs', I am afraid, but I still cannot understand from what file our shipping department got your address as 165 West 11th Street. I have removed the 57th Street address from the files and also the Arkansas address and I trust that we will not disturb your tranquillity further up there in Cornwall. It must be lovely this time of year in Virginia and I envy you and Mrs Thurber. Have a lovely time at The Homestead.

Sincerely yours,

ALMA WINEGE

PS. What you had to say about *Grandma* amused us all.

A.W.

COLUMBUS, OHIO
16 November 1949

Dear Mr Thurber,

I have decided to come right out with the little problem that was accidentally dumped in my lap yesterday. I hope you will forgive me for what happened, and perhaps you can suggest what I should do with the books. There are three dozen of them and, unfortunately, they arrived when my little son Donald was alone downstairs. By the time I found out about the books, he had torn off the wrappings and had built a cute little house out of them. I have placed them all on a shelf out of his reach while awaiting word as to where to send them. I presume I could ship them to you C.O.D. if I can get somebody to wrap them properly.

I heard from old Mrs Winston next door that you and your family once lived here at 568 Oak Street. She remembers you and your brothers as cute little tykes who were very noisy and raised rabbits and guinea-pigs. She says your mother was a wonderful cook. I am sorry about Donald opening the books and I hope you will forgive him.

Sincerely yours,
CLARA EDWARDS
(MRS J. C.)

WEST CORNWALL, CONN.
19 November 1949

Mr Leon Charteriss,
The Charteriss Publishing Co.,
132 East What Street,
New York, N.Y.

Dear Mr Charteriss,

I am enclosing a letter from a Mrs J. C. Edwards, of Columbus, Ohio, in the fervent hope that you will do something to stop this insane flux of books. I never ordered these books. I have not read *Grandma Was a Nudist*. I do not intend to read it. I want something done to get these volumes off my trail and cut out of my consciousness.

I have written Miss Winege about the situation, but I am afraid to take it up with her again, because she might send them to me in care of the Department of Journalism at Ohio State University, where I was a student more than thirty years ago.

Sincerely yours,
J. THURBER

200

PS. I never use my middle initial, but your firm seems to think it is 'M'. It is not.

                                                              J.T.

              THE CHARTERISS PUBLISHING COMPANY
                      NEW YORK, N.Y.
                                              23 November 1949
Mr James M. Thurber,
West Cornwall, Conn.

Dear Mr Thurber,
    Mr Charteriss has flown to California on a business trip and will be gone for several weeks. His secretary has turned your letter of the 19th over to me. I have asked Mr Cluffman to write to Miss Clara Edwards in Columbus and arrange for the reshipment of the thirty-six copies of *Grandma Was a Nudist*.
    I find, in consulting the records, that you have three times ordered copies of your own book, *Thurber's Ark*, to be shipped to you at West Cornwall, at the usual discount rate of forty per cent. I take it that what you really wanted was thirty-six copies of your own book and they are being sent out to you today with our regrets for the discomfit we have caused you. I hope you will be a little patient with us during this so trying period of reorganisation.

                                          Cordially yours,
                                       JEANNETTE GAINES
                                          Stock Order Dept

PS. You will be happy to know that we have traced down the gentleman who ordered those copies of *Grandma*.

                                    WEST CORNWALL, CONN.
                                          25 November 1949
Mr Henry Johnson,
The Charteriss Pub. Co.,
New York, N.Y.

Dear Harry,
    Since the reorganisation at Charteriss, I have the forlorn and depressing feeling that I no longer know anybody down there

except you. I know that this immediate problem of mine is not in your field, but I turn to you as a last resource. What I want, or rather what I don't want, is simple enough, Harry. God knows it is simple.

I don't want any more copies of my book. I don't want any more copies of my book. I don't want any more copies of my book.

As ever,

JIM

PS. It has just occurred to me that I haven't seen you for more than two years. Let's have a drink one of these days. I'll give you a ring the next time I'm in the city.

J.T.

THE CHARTERISS PUBLISHING COMPANY

NEW YORK, N.Y.

26 November 1949

Mr James Grover Thurber,
Cornwall, Conn.

Dear Jim Thurber,

I haven't had the pleasure of meeting you since I had the great good luck to join forces with Charteriss, but I look forward to our meeting with a high heart. Please let me know the next time you are in the city, as I should like to wine and dine you and perhaps discuss the new book that I feel confident you have in you. If you don't want to talk shop, we can discuss the record of our mutual football team. You were at Northwestern some years ahead of my time, I believe, but I want you to know that they still talk about Jimmy Thurber out there.

Your letter to Harry Johnson has just come to my attention, and I regret to say that Harry is no longer with us. He went to Simon and Schuster in the summer of 1948. I want you to feel, however, that every single one of us here is your friend, willing and eager to drop everything to do your slightest bidding. All of us feel very deeply about your having turned against your book *Thurber's Ark*. I note that in your present mood you have the feeling that you never want to see it again. Well, Jim, let me assure you that this is just a passing fancy, derived from a moment of depression. When you put in your last order for thirty-six copies, you must surely have had some definite use in mind for them, and I am banking on twenty years' experience in the book-publishing game when I take the liberty of sending these thirty-six books off to you today. There is one thing I am something of an expert at, if I do say so myself, and that is the understanding of the 'creative spirit'.

We have a new system here, which is to send our authors not ten free copies, as of old, but fifteen. Therefore, five of the thirty-six copies will reach you with our compliments. The proper deductions will be made on the record.

Don't forget our dinner date.

Cordially,
CLINT JORDAN

PS. I approve of your decision to resume the use of your middle names. It gives a book dignity and flavour to use all three names. I think it was old Willa Cather who started the new trend, when she dropped the Seibert.

C.J

THE CHARTERISS PUBLISHING COMPANY
NEW YORK, N.Y.

13 December 1949

Dear Thurber,

Just back at the old desk after a trip to California and a visit with my mother, who is eighty-nine now but as chipper as ever. She would make a swell Profile. Ask me about her someday.

Need I say I was delighted to hear from the staff when I got back about your keen interest in *Grandma Was a Nudist*? The book has been moving beautifully and its ceiling has gone sky-high. We're planning a brief new advertising campaign and I'd be tickled pink if you would be good enough to bat out a blurb for us.

Yours,
LEON

15 December 1949

Mr James M. Thurber,
West Cornwall, Conn.

Dear Mr Thurber,
   I hope you will forgive me – indeed, all of us – for having inexcusably mislaid the address of the lady to whom the thirty-six copies of *Grandma Was a Nudist* were sent by mistake. I understand that we have already dispatched to you at your home another thirty-six volumes of that book.
   My apologies again.

Sincerely yours,
H. F. CLUFFMAN

WEST CORNWALL, CONN.
19 December 1949

Mr H. F. Cluffman,
The Charteriss Publishing Co.,
132 East What Street,
New York, N.Y.

Dear Mr Cluffman,
   The lady's name is Mrs J. C. Edwards, and she lives at 568 Oak Street, Columbus, Ohio.
   I have explained as clearly as I could in previous letters that I did not order thirty-six copies of *Grandma Was a Nudist*. If you have actually shipped to me another thirty-six copies of this book, it will make a total of seventy-two copies, none of which I will pay for. The thirty-six copies of *Thurber's Ark* that Mr Jordan has written me he intends to send to West Cornwall would bring up to one hundred and eight the total number of books that your firm, by a conspiracy of confusion unique even in the case of publishers, has mistakenly charged to my account. You may advise Mr Jordan that I do not wish to receive the five free copies he mentioned in his letter.

If your entire staff of employees went back to *Leslie's Weekly*, where they belong, it would set my mind at rest.

Sincerely yours,
J. THURBER

PS. I notice that you use only my middle initial, 'M'. Mr Jordan and I – or was it Mr Charteriss? – have decided to resume the use of the full name, which is Murfreesboro.

J.T.

WEST CORNWALL, CONN.
27 December 1949

Mr Leon Charteriss,
The Charteriss Publishing Co.,
132 East What Street,
New York, N.Y.

Dear Mr Charteriss,

I am sure you will be sorry to learn that Mr Thurber has had one of his spells as a result of the multiplication of books and misunderstanding that began with Miss Alma Winege's letter of 25 October 1949. Those of us around Mr Thurber are greatly disturbed by the unfortunate circumstances that have caused him to give up writing, at least temporarily, just after he had resumed work following a long fallow period.

Thirty-six copies of Mr Thurber's book and thirty-six copies of *Grandma Was a Nudist* have arrived at his home here, and he has asked me to advise you that he intends to burn all seventy-two. West Cornwall is scarcely the community for such a demonstration – he proposes to burn them in the middle of U.S. Highway No. 7 – since the town regards with a certain suspicion any writer who has not won a Pulitzer Prize. I am enclosing copies of all the correspondence between your company and Mr Thurber, in the hope that someone connected with your firm will read it with proper care and intelligence and straighten out this deplorable and inexcusable situation.

Mr Thurber wishes me to tell you that he does not want to hear from any of you again.

Sincerely yours,
ELLEN BAGLEY
Secretary to Mr Thurber

28 December 1949

Mr James Murfreesboro Thurber,
72 West,
Cornwall, Conn.

Dear Mr Thurber,
   I have at hand your letter of December 19th, the opening paragraph of which puzzles me. You send me the following name and address – Mrs J. C. Edwards, 568 Oak Street, Columbus, Ohio – but it is not clear what use you wish me to make of this. I would greatly appreciate it if you would clear up this small matter for me.

                                        Sincerely yours,
                                        H. F. CLUFFMAN

PS. *Leslie's Weekly* ceased publication many years ago. I could obtain the exact date if you so desire.

                                        H.F.C.

29 December 1949

Mr James M. Thurber,
West Cornwall, Conn.

Dear Mr Thurber,
   You will be sorry to hear that Mr Charteriss was taken suddenly ill with a virus infection. His doctor believes that he lost his immunity during his visit to the West Coast. He is now in the hospital, but his condition is not serious.
   Since the departure of Miss Gaines, who was married last week, I have taken over the Stock Order Department for the time being. I did not take the liberty of reading your enclosures in the letter to Mr Charteriss, but sent them directly to him at the hospital. I am sure that he will be greatly cheered up by them when he is well enough to read. Meanwhile, I want you to know that you can repose all confidence in the

Stock Order Department to look after your needs, whatever they may be.

Sincerely yours,
GLADYS MACLEAN

PS. I learned from Mr Jordan that you were a friend of Willa Cather's. Exciting!

COLUMBUS, OHIO
3 January 1950

Dear Jamie,

I don't understand the clipping from the Lakeville *Journal* Helen's mother sent me, about someone burning all those books of yours in the street. I never heard of such a thing, and don't understand how they could have taken the books without your knowing it, or what you were doing with so many copies of the novel about the naked grandmother. Imagine, at her age! She couldn't carry on like that in Columbus, let me tell you. Why, when I was a girl, you didn't dare walk with a man after sunset, unless he was your husband, and even then there was talk.

It's a good thing that state policeman came along in time to save most of the books from being completely ruined, and you must be thankful for the note Mr Jordan put in one of the books, for the policeman would never have known who they belonged to if he hadn't found it.

A Mrs Edwards phoned this morning and said that her son Donald collects your books and wants to send them to you – to be autographed, I suppose. Her son has dozens of your books and I told her you simply wouldn't have time to sign all of them, and she said she didn't care what you did with them. And then she said they weren't your books at all, and so I just hung up on her.

Be sure to bundle up when you go out.

With love,
MOTHER

PS. This Mrs Edwards says she lives at 568 Oak Street. I told her we used to live there and she said God knows she was aware of that. I don't know what she meant. I was afraid this little boy would send you all those books to sign and so I told his mother that you and Helen were at The Homestead, in Hot Springs. You don't suppose he would send them there, do you?

and here, gentle reader, I know you will be glad to leave all of us.

MY OWN TEN RULES FOR A HAPPY MARRIAGE

Nobody, I hasten to announce, has asked me to formulate a set of rules for the perpetuation of marital bliss and the preservation of the tranquil American boudoir and inglenook. The idea just came to me one day, when I watched a couple in an apartment across the court from mine gesturing and banging tables and throwing *objets d'art* at each other. I couldn't hear what they were saying, but it was obvious, as the shot-put followed the hammer throw, that he and/or she (as the lawyers would put it) had deeply offended her and/or him.

Their apartment, before they began to take it apart, had been quietly and tastefully arranged, but it was a little hard to believe this now, as he stood there by the fireplace, using an andiron to bat back the Royal Doulton figurines she was curving at him from her strongly entrenched position behind the davenport. I wondered what had started the exciting but costly battle, and, brooding on the general subject of Husbands and Wives, I found myself compiling my own Ten Rules for a Happy Marriage.

I have avoided the time-worn admonitions, such as 'Praise her new hat', 'Share his hobbies', 'Be a sweetheart as well as a wife', and 'Don't keep a blonde in the guest-room', not only because they are threadbare from repetition, but also because they don't seem to have accomplished their purpose. Maybe what we need is a brand-new set of rules. Anyway, ready or not, here they come, the result of fifty years (I began as a little boy) spent in studying the nature and behaviour, mistakes and misunderstandings, of the American Male (*homo Americansis*) and his Mate.

RULE I: Neither party to a sacred union should run down, disparage, or badmouth the other's former girls or beaux, as the case may be. The tendency to attack the character, looks, intelligence, capability, and achievements of one's mate's former friends of the opposite sex is a common cause of domestic discontent. Sweetheart-slurring, as we will call this deplorable practice, is encouraged by a long spell of gloomy weather, too many highballs, hangovers, and the suspicion that one's spouse is hiding, and finding, letters in a hollow tree, or is intercepting the postman, or putting in secret phone-calls from the corner drugstore. These fears almost always turn out to be unfounded, but the unfounded fear, as we all know, is worse than the founded.

Aspersions, insinuations, reflections, or just plain cracks about old boy friends and girl friends should be avoided at all times. Here are some of the expressions that should be especially eschewed: 'That waffle-fingered, minor-league third baseman you latched on to at Cornell'; 'You know the girl I mean – the one with the hips who couldn't read'; 'That old flame of yours with the vocabulary of a hoot owl'; and 'You remember her – that old bat who chewed gum and dressed like Daniel Boone.'

This kind of derogatory remark, if persisted in by one or both parties to a marriage, will surely lead to divorce or, at best, a blow on the head with a glass ash-tray.

RULE II: A man should make an honest effort to get the names of his wife's friends right. This is not easy. The average wife who was graduated from college at any time during the past thirty years keeps in close touch with at least seven old classmates. These ladies, known as 'the girls', are named, respectively: Mary, Marian, Melissa, Marjorie, Maribel, Madeleine, and Miriam; and all of them are called Myrtle by the careless husband we are talking about. Furthermore, he gets their nicknames wrong. This, to be sure, is understandable, since their nicknames are, respectively: Molly, Muffy, Missy, Midge, Mabby, Maddy, and Mims. The careless husband, out of thoughtlessness or pure cussedness, calls them all Mugs, or, when he is feeling particularly brutal, Mucky.

All the girls are married, one of them to a Ben Tompkins, and as this is the only one he can remember, our hero calls all the husbands Ben, or Tompkins, adding to the general annoyance and confusion.

If you are married to a college graduate, then, try to get the names of her girl friends and their husbands straight. This will prevent some of those interminable arguments that begin after Midge and Harry (not Mucky and Ben) have said a stiff good night and gone home.

RULE III: A husband should not insult his wife publicly, at parties. He should insult her in the privacy of the home. Thus, if a man thinks the soufflés his wife makes are as tough as an outfielder's glove, he should tell her so when they are at home, not when they are out at a formal dinner party where a perfect soufflé has just been served. The same rule applies to the wife. She should not regale his men friends, or women friends, with hilarious accounts of her husband's clumsiness, remarking that he dances like a 1907 Pope Hartford, or that he locked himself in the children's rabbit pen and couldn't get out. All parties must end finally, and the husband or wife who has revealed all may find that there is hell to pay in the taxi going home.

RULE IV: The wife who keeps saying, 'Isn't that just like a man?' and the husband who keeps saying, 'Oh, well, you know how women are,' are likely to grow further and further apart through the years. These famous generalisations have the effect of reducing an individual to the anonymous status of a mere unit in a mass. The wife who, just in time, comes upon her husband about to fry an egg in a dry skillet should not classify him with all other males but should give him the accolade of a special distinction. She might say, for example, 'George, no other man in the world would try to do a thing like that.' Similarly, a husband watching his wife labouring to start the car without turning on the ignition should not say to the gardener or a passer-by, 'Oh, well, you know, etc.' Instead, he should remark to his wife, 'I've seen a lot of women in my life, Nellie, but I've never seen one who could touch you.'

Certain critics of this rule will point out that the specific comments I would substitute for the old familiar generalities do not solve the problem. They will maintain that the husband and wife will be sore and sulky for several days, no matter what is said. One wife, reading Rule IV over my shoulder, exclaimed, 'Isn't that just like a man?' This brings us right back where we started. Oh, well, you know how women are!

RULE V: When a husband is reading aloud, a wife should sit quietly in her chair, relaxed but attentive. If he has decided to read the Republican platform, an article on elm blight, or a blow-by-blow account of a prize fight, it is not going to be easy, but she should at least pretend to be interested. She should not keep swinging one foot, start to wind her wrist-watch, file her fingernails, or clap her hands in an effort to catch a mosquito. The good wife allows the mosquito to bite her when her husband is reading aloud.

She should not break in to correct her husband's pronunciation, or to tell him one of his socks is wrong side out. When the husband has finished, the wife should not lunge instantly into some irrelevant subject. It's wiser to exclaim 'How interesting!' or, at the very least, 'Well, well!' She might even compliment him on his diction and his grasp of politics, elm blight, or boxing. If he should ask some shrewd question to test her attention, she can cry, 'Good heavens!' leap up, and rush out to the kitchen on some urgent fictitious errand. This may fool him, or it may not. I hope, for her sake – and his – that it does.

RULE VI: A husband should try to remember where things are around the house so that he does not have to wait for his wife to get home from the hairdresser's before he can put his hands on what he wants. Among the things a husband is usually unable to locate are the iodine, the aspirin, the nail file, the French vermouth, his cuff links, studs, black silk socks and evening shirts, the snapshots taken at Nantucket last summer, his favourite record of 'Kentucky Babe', the borrowed copy of *My Cousin Rachel*, the garage key, his own towel, the last bill from Brooke Bros., his pipe cleaners, the poker chips, crackers, cheese, the whetstone, his new raincoat, and the screens for the upstairs windows.

I don't really know the solution to this problem, but one should be found. Perhaps every wife should draw for her husband a detailed map of the house, showing clearly the location of everything he might need. Trouble is, I suppose, he would lay the map down somewhere and not be able to find it until his wife got home.

RULE VII: If a husband is not listening to what his wife is saying, he should not grunt, 'Okay' or 'Yeah, sure', or make little affirmative noises. A husband lost in thought or worry is likely not to take in the sense of such a statement as this: 'We're going to the Gordons for dinner tonight, John, so I'm letting the servants off. Don't come home from the office first. Remember, we both have to be at the dentist's at five, and I'll pick you up there with the car.' Now, an 'Okay' or a 'Yeah, sure' at this point can raise havoc if the husband hasn't really been listening. As usual, he goes all the way out to his home in Glenville – thirteen miles from the dentist's office and seventeen miles from the Gordons' house – and he can't find his wife. He can't find the servants. His wife can't get him on the phone because all she gets is the busy buzz. John is calling everybody he can think of except, of course, in his characteristic way, the dentist and the Gordons. At last he hangs up, exhausted and enraged. Then the phone rings. It is his wife. And there let us leave them.

RULE VIII: If your husband ceases to call you 'Sugarfoot' or 'Candy Eyes' or 'Cutie Fudge Pie' during the first year of your marriage, it is not necessarily a sign that he has come to take you for granted or that he no longer cares. It is probably an indication that he has recovered his normal perspective. Many a young husband who once called his wife 'Tender Mittens' or 'Taffy Ears' or 'Rose Lips' has become austere or important, like a Common Pleas Judge, and he wouldn't want reports of his youthful frivolity to get around. If he doesn't call you Dagmar when your name is Daisy, you are sitting pretty.

RULE IX: For those whose husbands insist on pitching for the Married Men against the Single Men at the Fourth-of-July picnic of the First M.E. Church, I have the following suggestion: don't sit on the sidelines and watch him. Get lost. George is sure to be struck out by a fourteen-year-old boy, pull up with a Charley horse running to first, and get his teeth knocked out by an easy grounder to the mound. When you see him after the game, tell him everybody knew the little boy was throwing illegal spitballs, everybody saw the first baseman spike George, and everybody said that grounder took such a nasty bounce even Phil Rizzuto couldn't have fielded it. Remember, most middle-aged husbands get to sleep at night by imagining they are striking out the entire batting order of the Yankees.

RULE X: A wife's dressing-table should be inviolable. It is the one place in the house a husband should get away from and stay away from. And yet, the average husband is drawn to it as by a magnet, especially when he is carrying something wet, oily, greasy, or sticky, such as a universal joint, a hub cap, or the blades of a lawn mower. His excuse for bringing these alien objects into his wife's bedroom in the first place is that he is looking for 'an old rag' with which to wipe them off. There are no old rags in a lady's boudoir, but husbands never seem to learn this. They search hampers, closets, and bureau drawers, expecting to find a suitable piece of cloth, but first they set the greasy object on the dressing-table. The aggrieved wife may be tempted, following this kind of vandalism, to lock her bedroom door and kick her husband out for good. I suggest, however, a less stringent punishment. Put a turtle in his bed. The wife who is afraid to pick up a turtle should ask Junior to help her. Junior will love it.

Now I realise, in glancing back over these rules, that some of my solutions to marital problems may seem a little untidy; that I have, indeed, left a number of loose ends here and there. For example, if the husbands are going to mislay their detailed maps of household objects, I have accomplished nothing except to add one item for the distraught gentleman to lose.

Then, there is that turtle. Captious critics will point out that a turtle in a husband's bed is not a valid solution to anything, but merely a further provocation. The outraged husband will deliberately trip his wife during their next mixed-doubles match. She will thereupon retaliate by putting salt in his breakfast coffee . . .

Let somebody else try to figure out what to do about the Running Feud in marriage. The Williamses are coming to dinner tonight, and I promised to put the white wine on the ice at three o'clock. It is now six-thirty. After all, I have my own problems.

THE FIGGERIN' OF AUNT WILMA

When I was a boy, John Hance's grocery stood on the south side of Town Street, just east of Fourth, in the Central Market region of Columbus, Ohio. It was an old store even then, forty-five years ago, and its wide oak floor boards had been worn pleasantly smooth by the shoe soles of three generations of customers. The place smelt of coffee, peppermint, vinegar, and spices. Just inside the door on the left, a counter with a rounded glass front held all the old-fashioned penny candies – gumdrops, liquorice whips, horehound, and the rest – some of them a little pale with age. On the rear wall, between a barrel of dill pickles and a keg of salt mackerel in brine, there was an iron coffee grinder, whose handle I was sometimes allowed to turn.

Once, Mr Hance gave me a stick of Yucatan gum, an astonishing act of generosity, since he had a sharp sense of the value of a penny. Thrift was John Hance's religion. His store was run on a strictly cash basis. He shared the cost of his telephone with the Hays Carriage Shop, next door. The instrument was set in a movable wooden cubicle that could be whirled through an opening in the west wall of the store. When I was ten, I used to hang around the grocery on Saturday afternoons, waiting for the telephone to disappear into the wall. Then I would wait for it to swing back again. It was a kind of magic, and I was disappointed to learn of its mundane purpose – the saving of a few dollars a month.

Mr Hance was nearly seventy, a short man with white hair and a white moustache and the most alert eyes that I can remember, except perhaps Aunt Wilma Hudson's. Aunt Wilma lived on South Sixth Street and always shopped at Mr Hance's store. Mr Hance's eyes were blue and capable of a keen concentration that could make you squirm. Aunt Wilma had black agate eyes that moved restlessly and scrutinised everybody with bright suspicion. In church, her glance would dart around the congregation seeking out irreverent men and women whose expressions showed that they were occupied with worldly concerns, or even carnal thoughts, in the holy place. If she lighted on a culprit, her heavy, dark brows would lower, and her mouth would tighten in righteous disapproval. Aunt Wilma was as honest as the day is long and as easily confused, when it came to what she called figgerin', as the night is dark. Her clashes with Mr Hance had become a family legend. He was a swift and competent calculator, and nearly fifty years of constant practice had enabled him to add up a column of figures almost at a glance. He set down his columns swiftly on an empty paper sack with a stubby black pencil. Aunt Wilma, on the other hand, was slow and painstaking when it came to figgerin'. She would go over and over a column of numbers, her glasses far down on her nose, her lips moving soundlessly. To her, rapid calculation, like all the other reckless and impulsive habits of men, was tainted with a kind of godlessness. Mr Hance always sighed when he looked up and saw her coming into his store. He knew that she could lift a simple dollar transaction into a dim and mystic realm of confusion all her own.

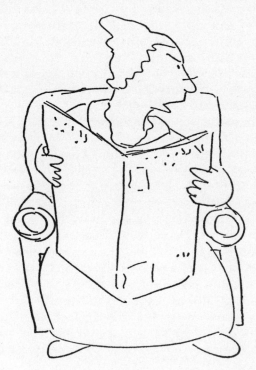

I was fortunate enough to be present one day in 1905 when Mr Hance's calculating and Aunt Wilma's figgerin' came together in memorable single combat. She had wheedled me into carrying her market basket, on the ground that it was going to be too heavy for her to manage. Her two grandsons, boys around my own age, had skipped out when I came to call at their house, and Aunt Wilma promptly seized on me. A young'un, as she called everybody under seventeen, was not worth his salt if he couldn't help a body about the house. I had shopped with her before, under duress, and I knew her accustomed and invariable route on Saturday mornings, when Fourth Street, from Main to State, was lined with the stands of truck gardeners. Prices were incredibly low in those days, but Aunt Wilma questioned the cost, the quality, and the measure of everything. By the time she had finished her long and tedious purchases of fresh produce from the country, and we had turned east into Town Street and headed for Mr Hance's store, the weight of the market basket was beginning to pain my arm. 'Come along, child, come along,' Aunt Wilma snapped, her eyes shining with the look of the Middle Western housewife engaged in hard but virtuous battle with the wicked forces of the merchandising world.

I saw Mr Hance make a small involuntary gesture with his right hand as he spied Aunt Wilma coming through the door. He had just finished with a customer, and since his assistant was busy, he knew he was in for it. It took a good half-hour for Aunt Wilma to complete her shopping for groceries, but at length everything she wanted was stacked on the counter in sacks and cans and boxes. Mr Hance set deftly to work with his paper sack and pencil, jotting down the price of each article as he fitted it into the basket. Aunt Wilma watched his expert movements closely, like a hostile baseball fan waiting for an error in the infield. She regarded adroitness in a man as 'slick' rather than skilful.

Aunt Wilma's purchases amounted to ninety-eight cents. After writing down this sum, Mr Hance, knowing my aunt, whisked the paper bag around on the counter so that she could examine his addition. It took her some time, bending over and peering through her glasses, to arrive at a faintly reluctant corroboration of his figgerin'. Even when she was satisfied that all was in order, she had another go at the column of numbers, her lips moving silently as she added them up for the third time. Mr Hance waited patiently, the flat of his hands on the counter. He seemed to be fascinated by the movement of her lips. 'Well, I guess it's all right,' said Aunt Wilma, at last, 'but everything *is* so dear.' What she had bought for less than a dollar made the market basket bulge. Aunt Wilma took her purse out of her bag and drew out a dollar bill slowly and handed it over, as if it were a hundred dollars she would never see again.

Mr Hance deftly pushed the proper keys of the cash register, and the red hand on the indicator pointed to $.98. He studied the cash drawer, which had shot out at him. 'Well, well,' he said, and then, 'Hmm. Looks like I haven't got any pennies.' He turned back to Aunt Wilma. 'Have you got three cents, Mrs Hudson?' he asked.

That started it.

Aunt Wilma gave him a quick look of distrust. Her Sunday suspicion gleamed in her eyes. '*You owe me two cents*,' she said sharply.

'I know that, Mrs Hudson,' he sighed, 'but I'm out of pennies. Now, if you'll give me three cents, I'll give you a nickel.'

Aunt Wilma stared at him cautiously.

'It's all right if you give him three cents and he gives you a nickel,' I said.

'Hush up,' said Aunt Wilma. 'I'm figgerin'.' She figgered for several moments, her mouth working again.

Mr Hance slipped a nickel out of the drawer and placed it on the counter. 'There is your nickel,' he said firmly. 'Now you just have to give me three cents.'

Aunt Wilma pecked about in her purse and located three pennies, which she brought out carefully, one at a time. She laid them on the counter beside the nickel, and Mr Hance reached for them. Aunt Wilma was too quick for him. She covered the eight cents with a lean hand. 'Wait, now!' she said, and she took her hand away slowly. She frowned over the four coins as if they were a difficult hand in bridge whist. She ran her lower lip against her upper teeth. 'Maybe if I give you a dime,' she said, 'and take the eight cents . . . It is *two* cents you're short, ain't it?'

Mr Hance began to show signs of agitation. One or two amused customers were now taking in the scene out of the corners of their eyes. 'No, no,' said Mr Hance. 'That way, you would be making me a present of seven cents!' This was too much for Aunt Wilma. She couldn't understand the new and preposterous sum of seven cents that had suddenly leaped at her from nowhere. The notion that she was about to do herself out of some money staggered her, and her eyes glazed for a moment like a groggy prizefighter's. Neither Mr Hance nor I said anything out of fear of deepening the tangle. She made an uncertain move of her right hand and I had the wild thought that she was going to give Mr Hance one of the pennies and scoop up the seven cents, but she didn't. She fell into a silent clinch with the situation and then her eyes cleared. 'Why, of *course!*' she cried brightly. 'I don't know what got into me! You take the eight cents and give me a dime. Then I'll have the two cents that's coming to me.' One of the customers laughed, and Aunt Wilma cut him down with a swift glare. The diversion gave me time to figure out that whereas Mr Hance had been about to gain seven cents, he was now going to lose a nickel. 'That way, *I* would be making *you* a present of *five* cents, Mrs Hudson,' he said stiffly. They stood motionless for several seconds, each trying to stare the other down.

'Now, here,' said Mr Hance, turning and taking her dollar out of the still open cash drawer. He laid it beside the nickel and the pennies. 'Now, here,' he said again. 'You gave me a dollar three, but you don't owe me a dollar three – you owe me five cents less than that. Here is the five cents.' He snatched it up and handed it to her. She held the nickel between thumb and forefinger, and her eyes gleamed briefly, as if she at last comprehended the peculiar deal, but the gleam faded. Suddenly she handed him his nickel and picked up her dollar and her three cents. She put the pennies back in her purse. 'I've rung up the ninety-eight cents, Mrs Hudson,' said Mr Hance quickly. 'I must put the dollar back in the till.' He turned and pointed at the $.98 on the indicator. 'I tell you what. If you'll give me the dollar, I'll give you the nickel and we'll call it square.' She obviously didn't want to take the nickel or give up the dollar, but she did, finally. I was astounded at first, for here was the penny-careful Mr Hance knocking three cents off a bill, but then I realised he was afraid of losing the dollar and was willing to settle for the lesser of two evils.

'Well,' said Aunt Wilma irritably, 'I'm sure I don't know what you're trying to do.' I was a timid boy, but I had to plunge into the snarl, if only on behalf of the family honour. 'Gee, Aunt Wilma,' I told her, 'if you keep the nickel, he's giving you everything for ninety-five cents.'

Mr Hance scowled hard at me. He was afraid I was going to get him in deeper than he already was. 'It's all right, son,' he said. 'It's all right.' He put the dollar in the till and shoved the drawer shut with a decisive bang, but I wasn't going to give up.

'Gee whizz, Aunt Wilma,' I complained, 'you still owe him three cents. Don't you see that?'

She gave me the pitying glance of a superior and tired intelligence. 'I never owed him three cents in my life,' she said tartly. 'He owes me two cents. You stay out of things you don't understand.'

'It's all right,' said Mr Hance again, in a weary voice. He was sure that if she scrabbled in her purse again for the three pennies, she would want her dollar back, and they would be right where they had started. I gave my aunt a look of disenchantment.

'Now, wait!' she cried suddenly. 'Maybe I have the exact change! I don't know what's got into me I didn't think of that! I think I have the right change after all.' She put back on the counter the nickel she had been clutching in her left hand, and then she began to peck at the coins in her purse and, after a good minute, arranged two quarters, four dimes, Mr Hance's nickel, and three pennies on the counter. 'There,' she said, her eyes flashing triumph. 'Now you give me my dollar back.'

Mr Hance sighed deeply, rang out the cash drawer by pushing 'No Sale', and handed her the dollar. Then he hastily scraped up the change, deposited each coin in its proper place in the till, and slammed the drawer shut again. I was only ten, and mathematics was not my best study, but it wasn't hard to figure that Mr Hance, who in the previous arrangement had been out three cents, was now out five cents. 'Good day, Mrs Hudson,' he said grimly. He felt my sympathetic eyes on him, and we exchanged a brief, knowing masculine glance of private understanding.

'Good day, Mr Hance,' said Aunt Wilma, and her tone was as grim as the grocer's.

I took the basket from the counter, and Mr Hance sighed again, this time with relief. 'Goodbye, goodbye,' he said with false heartiness, glad to see us on our way. I felt I should slip him the parsley, or whatever sack in the basket had cost a nickel.

'Come on, child,' said Aunt Wilma. 'It's dreadfully late. I declare it's taken hours to shop today.' She muttered plaintively all the way out of the store.

I noticed as I closed the door behind us that Mr Hance was waiting on a man customer. The man was laughing. Mr Hance frowned and shrugged.

As we walked east on Town Street, Aunt Wilma let herself go. 'I never heard of such a thing in all the born days of my life,' she said. 'I don't know where John Hance got his schooling, if he got any. The very idea – a grown man like that getting so mixed up. Why, I could have spent the whole day in that store and he'd never of figgered it out. Let him keep the two cents, then. It was worth it to get out of that store.'

'*What* two cents, Aunt Wilma?' I almost squealed.

'Why, the two cents he still owes me!' she said. 'I don't know what they teach you young'uns nowadays. Of course he owes me two cents. It come to ninety-eight cents and I give him a dollar. He owed me two cents in the beginning and he still owes me two cents. Your Uncle Herbert will explain it to you. Any man in the world could figger it out except John Hance.'

I walked on beside her in silence, thinking of Uncle Herbert, a balding, choleric man of high impatience and quick temper.

'Now, you let *me* explain it to your Uncle Herbert, child,' she said. 'I declare you were as mixed up as John Hance was. If I'd of listened to you and given him the three cents, like you said, I'd never of got my dollar back. He'd owe me five cents instead of two. Why, it's as plain as day.'

I thought I had the solution for her now, and I leaped at it. 'That's right, Aunt Wilma,' I almost yelled. 'He owed you a nickel and he gave you the nickel.'

Aunt Wilma stabbed me with her indignation. 'I gave *him* the nickel,' she said. 'I put it on the counter right there under your very eyes, and you saw him scoop it up.'

I shifted the market basket to my left arm. 'I know, Aunt Wilma,' I said, 'but it was *his* nickel all the time.'

She snorted. 'Well, he's got his precious nickel, ain't he?' she demanded. I shifted the basket again. I thought I detected a faint trace of uneasiness in her tone. She fell silent and quickened her cadence, and it was hard for me to keep up with her. As we turned south into Sixth Street, I glanced up and saw that she was frowning and that her lips were moving again. She was rehearsing the story of the strange transaction for Uncle Herbert. I began to whistle. 'Hush up, child,' she said. 'I'm figgerin'.'

Uncle Herbert was sitting in the living-room, eating an apple. I could tell from his expression that he was in one of his rare amiable moods. Aunt Wilma grabbed the basket away from me. 'Now, you let me explain it to your uncle,' she said. 'You wait till I get back.' She sailed out of the room on her way to the kitchen.

A little breathlessly, I told Uncle Herbert the saga of Aunt Wilma's complicated financial quandary. He was chuckling when she came back into the room.

Uncle Herbert's amusement nettled her. 'The boy got it wrong,' she said accusingly. 'He didn't tell it right. He was ever' bit as mixed up as John Hance.' Uncle Herbert's chuckle increased to full and open laughter. Aunt Wilma glared at him until he subsided. 'Now, Herbert, you listen to me,' she began, but he cut in on her.

'If Hance ever gives you that two cents he owes you, Wilma,' he said, 'I tell you what you have to do to square accounts. Someday you're going to have to give him a dime for three cents.' He began to laugh again.

Aunt Wilma Hudson stared at each of us in turn, with a look of fine, cold scorn, and then she raised both her hands and let them fall helplessly. 'I declare,' she said, 'I don't know how the world gets along with the men runnin' it.'

HOW TO GET THROUGH THE DAY

'How do you get through the day?' a woman out in Iowa has asked me in a letter. I can't tell whether she wants help in getting through her own day, or whether she has made a wager with somebody that I don't get through my own day at all, but somehow contrive to bypass it. The truth is that I do get through the day and, if it will benefit anybody, I shall be glad to state how I manage it. It might be simpler to put my method in the form of rules.

One: Never answer a telephone that rings before breakfast. It is sure to be one of three types of persons that is calling: a strange man in Minneapolis who has been up all night and is phoning collect; a salesman who wants to come over and demonstrate a new, patented combination dictaphone and music box that also cleans rugs; or a woman out of one's past. Just let the phone ring. The woman would be sure to say:

'This is Thelma Terwilliger. What are you going to *do* about me?' If you talk to her before your orange juice and coffee, or even afterwards, for that matter, you will never get through the day. Professors Radnor and Grube, in their monumentally depressing treatise, *The Female of the Species*, list a total of 1,113 possible involvements with a woman, all but eight of them ranging from the untoward to the inextricable.

223

Two: If you want to keep your breakfast down, do not read the front page, or any page, of the morning newspaper. Fifteen years ago the late Professor Herman Allen Miller of Ohio State University wrote me that, out there, no news was the only good news. He would be saddened, but not surprised, to learn that nowadays no news is the only good news anywhere. It is better to dip into *The Last Days of Pompeii* than to peruse the morning paper at breakfast, but what I do is turn on WQXR for classical or semi-classical music, or WPAT for popular music out of the late-lamented American past – such songs, for example, as 'Whispering', 'Sleepy Time Gal', 'Sunny', and 'Honey, Honey, Bless Your Heart'. (If you have been foolish enough to talk with Thelma, the last two songs will probably become 'Money', and 'Money, Money, Bless Your Heart'.) One morning, by mistake, I got another station than WPAT and listened, relaxed, to a recording of 'People Will Say We're in Love', sung by Alfred Drake and Joan Roberts, when suddenly it terminated and a young detergent voice began yelling:

'Don't knock rock 'n' roll, it's a rockin' good way to mess around and fall in love.' What have we done to deserve this? Or should I say, what have we done not to deserve it?

Three: Avoid the ten-o'clock news on the radio, at all costs. It is always confined to disasters – automobile accidents involving seventeen cars, the fatal stabbing of a fourteen-year-old girl by her twelve-year-old sweetheart, attacks on young mothers in Brooklyn basements, and riotous demonstrations by 15,000 students in Graustark. It is comforting, in a vaguely uneasy way, to realise that American students do not engage in political demonstrations, but reserve their passions for panty raids, jazz festivals, and the hanging of football coaches in effigy.

Four: Do not open the morning mail when it arrives if you are alone in the house. If I am alone when my mail arrives, around eleven o'clock, I wait for my wife to get back from the hairdresser. If she says, 'God!' or 'Oh, no!' after glancing at a letter, I hastily tell her to send it on to our lawyer or our agent, without reading it to me. I now get about twelve letters every morning, and she is happy if not more than two of them call for wedding presents. About seven of the twelve always call for something, and you ought to consider yourself lucky that you are not me. I am asked to read something, to write something, to send something, to do something, to explain something, or to go somewhere. These letters invariably begin like this: 'I realise that you are a very busy man, but . . .' and they always end: 'Thanks for your time and trouble.' I am pleased to report that at least two letters every day are intelligent, warm, and even humorous, and that they almost invariably come from American wives and mothers unknown to me, who frequently say, 'I love you.' This cheers me up enormously, until I begin thinking about Thelma Terwilliger again.

Five: Some years ago a distinguished American woman physician recommended 'a nap after lunch and a nip before dinner'. I myself do not recommend the nap after lunch, except for infants. My researches among those who have tried it show that eighty per cent of the males and one hundred per cent of the females just lie there wide-eyed, strumming the headboard with their fingers and/or, as the lawyers say, moaning low. Among the thoughts that keep Americans awake are – but why should I list them, sleepless reader, when you know what they are as well as I do?

As for the nip before dinner, I'm all for it, unless it leads to a nipping that doesn't end until after three o'clock in the morning. Speaking of tranquillisers, which everybody always is, I do not turn to Miltown, but to Milton, and to some of the other bards sublime, and a few of the humbler poets. Because of the distressing process of mental association, however, poetry is not always a help. The other morning, for example, I got to Edna St Vincent Millay's 'There isn't a train I wouldn't take, no matter where it's going' when it suddenly turned into, 'There isn't a train that I can take, no matter where I'm going.' This disturbing paraphrase grew out of a seven-weeks' period of travel in the Middle West last winter, during which I had to be driven by car from Columbus, Ohio, to Detroit because the only train out of the Ohio capital for the great Michigan city leaves at 4 a.m. I also found it simpler to be driven from Detroit to Cleveland, since railroad transportation in the Middle West has regressed to about where it was at the time of Custer's Last Stand.

The trouble with turning to verse while nipping before dinner, especially in a public place like the lobby of the Hotel

Algonquin, is that one is likely to grow irritable, or even bitter, instead of leaning back and relaxing in one's chair. A playwright I know, who tried repeating lines of Longfellow to himself in the Algonquin lobby at six o'clock one evening, was abruptly impelled, while nipping his fourth martini, to accost a strange lady and proclaim, 'I say the struggle naught availeth, madam,' after which he turned to a male stranger and snarled, 'Life is but an empty dream, Mac.' He then returned to his own chair. All of a sudden he spotted a poet across the lobby, and he was upon him in a moment, saying, 'Hell with thee, blythe spirit, bard thou never wert.' When the rude fellow later told me, proudly, what he had said, I could only snarl, on my own fourth nip before dinner, 'I am glad you did not once see Shelley plain, and did not stop and talk to him.'

Six: This brings us to the dinner hour and the problem of getting through *that*. Here everybody has to work out his own system of getting his dinner down, and keeping it down. Dinner-table conversation should be selected with great care nowadays since the first seventeen subjects that spring to mind are likely to be gloomy, running from the muddle-fuddle of international relations to the dangers of cholesterol and diester stilvesterol, and if you don't know what they are, I'm not going to tell you. My wife and I, Monday through Friday, usually dine in our own home with thirteen and a half million and one Americans, the thirteen and a half million members of the

C.I.O.A.F. of L. who sponsor the commentator Edward P. Morgan on WABC at 7 p.m., and Mr Morgan himself. The good, strong voice of Elmer Davis is no longer heard in the land, but Mr Morgan carries on ably in his stead, with the same intelligence, devotion to American ideals, courage, and wit. One night, during Christmas week of 1959, he discussed the lavish, expensive, and empty celebration of Holy Week and said, 'We seem to forget that Christ was born in a manger and not in the Bethlehem-Hilton.' It is a thought to remember.

Seven: Tender is the night no more, as we all know, especially the summer night, and when it falls, I always think of Robert Benchley's provocative title, 'What To Do When It Gets Dark'. Most married couples, I have found out, totter to the television set and turn it on, but I would rather read something restful instead, like *The Naked and the Dead*. It is perhaps enough to say of the Westerns, that endless series of morbid discharges, that they inspired a certain little girl's definition of a hung jury as, 'Twelve men hanging from a tree'. As for the police bang-bangs, they seem more and more given over to the theory that most killers in our society are women, so that as soon as a demure wife or ex-wife appears on the scene, you can be pretty sure that she did it. She usually confesses, at the end, in a quiet voice, saying, simply, 'Yes, Lieutenant, I killed him.' This may not give *you* the creeps, but it gives *me* the creeps.

Eight: This brings us to beddy-bye. Well, good night, and I pray the Lord your soul to keep. My own nocturnal problem in the summertime consists of flying creatures, great big June bugs, or bang-sashes. One of them banged the sash of the window nearest my bed around midnight in July, and I leaped out of sleep and out of bed. 'It's just a bat,' said my wife reassuringly, and I sighed with relief. 'Thank God for that,' I said. 'I thought it was a human being.'

HOW TO TELL A FINE OLD WINE

In spite of all that has been written about wines, the confusion in the minds of some lay drinkers is just as foggy as it was – in the case of some minds, even foggier. The main trouble, I think, is that the average wine connoisseur has suddenly become rather more the writing man than the sipping man without possessing that fine precision in expository composition which comes only from long years of writing, rewriting, cutting down, and, most especially, throwing away. It is my hope in this article, somehow or other, to clear up a few of the more involved problems of nomenclature and of geographical (or viticultural) distribution, for I believe I know what the wine experts have been trying to say and I believe I can say it perhaps a little more clearly.

France, then, is divided into ninety different *Départements*, all but four of them ending in '*et-Oise*' (and-Oise) and twenty-seven of them having towns named Châlons. Fortunately, in only three of the Châlons *communes* are there *girondes* where any of the great wines of France are grown. We can safely confine ourselves to the Bordeaux region and the Burgundy region, respectively the *Côte-d'Or* and the *Côte de Châlons*, or as the French trainmen say, '*L'autre côté!*' The great wines of France are divided into only three classifications with which we need to be concerned: the *grands vins*, the *petits vins*, and the *vins fins*. And it is with the last that we shall be most particularly concerned. *Vins fins* means, simply enough, 'finished wines', that is, wines which did not turn out as well as might have been expected. It is these wines and none others which America is getting today and which America is going to continue to get. Just what causes this I don't exactly know, but something.

In the old days of the great *châteauxiers*, there was never any question about what to do with a *vin* when it turned out to be *fin*. The *châteauxiers* simply referred to it philosophically as '*fin de siècle*' (finished for good) and threw it out. They would have nothing to do with a wine that wasn't noble, distinguished, dignified, courageous, high-souled, and austere. Nowadays it is different. The *vins fins* are filtered through to the American public in a thousand different disguises, all spurious – not a genuine disguise among them. It is virtually impossible for the layman, when he picks up a bottle labelled 'St Julien-Clos Vougeot-Grandes Veuves, 1465A21, *mise du château*, Perdolio, Premier Cru, Marchanderie: Carton et Cie, 1924', to know whether he is getting, as should be the case with this label, a truly noble St Estèphe or, as is more likely to be the case, a Benicarló that has been blended with Heaven only knows what, perhaps even a white Margelaise! Well then, how *is* he to know?

Let us say that a bottle has come into our hands labelled as above. 'St Julien' is simply the name of the *commune* and 'Clos Vougeot' the name of the château around which the grapes are grown. 'Grandes Veuves' is either an added distinguishing flourish put on the noble old label years and years ago by some *grandes veuves* (large widows) or it is a meaningless addition placed thereon since repeal by those French *flâneurs* who hope to inveigle the American public into buying cheap and tawdry wines under elaborate and impressive-sounding labels. So much for the name of the wine itself.

The number, 1465A21, is nothing to be bewildered by. It is simply the official *estampe française de la douane* and it can be checked against the authentic 'serial-running' of the official French revenue stamping machine by applying to somebody in the French Embassy here, or the French Consulate, and asking him to get in touch with the man in charge of the registered files of the French revenue stamping department. If the letter used (in this case 'A') proves to be the actual letter employed in 1924 by the revenue stampers, the vintage date on the bottle is authentic, providing, of course, that the identifying letter was, in that year, inserted between the fourth and fifth figures of the serial number and that 146521 fell among the *estampages* allocated to the St Julien *commune* in that year. It is, of course, unfortunate that the Stavisky affair in France threw all the numbers in that country into the wildest sort of confusion, so that it is hardly likely that any stamp numbers can be certified with confidence by anybody for the next six months or so. But

the wine will be all the better after six months and France may be then have its records in order once more, if she can find them.

The phrase 'mise du château' is extremely simple, and it is astonishing how many Americans are puzzled by it. It means nothing more than 'mice in the château', just as it says. The expression goes back to the days, some twenty years ago, when certain French manufacturers of popular 'tonic wines' made fortunes almost overnight and in many cases bought up old châteaux, tore them down, and built lavish new ones in the rococo manner. These new châteaux were, of course, clean and well kept, but so garish and ugly that a disdainful expression grew up among the French peasantry in regard to them: 'Ils n'ont jamais de mise du château là-bas' ('They never have any mice in that château over there'). The grand old châteauxiers thereupon began to add to their labels, 'mise du château' – in other words, 'There are mice in this château', a proud if slightly incongruous legend for a bottle of noble old wine.

The label symbol 'Perdolio' on our bottle might equally well have been 'Manfreda', 'Variola', 'Muscatel', 'Amontillado', 'Sauternes', 'Katerina', or any one of a couple of hundred others. The idea of this name originated with the old Spanish vinteriosos, especially those of Casanovia and Valencia, and indicated simply a desire on the part of a given merchant to place the name of a favourite daughter, son, mistress, or wine on the bottles he merchandised.

'Premier Cru', which we come to next in looking back at our St Julien label, means 'first growth', that is, wine that was grown first. And 'Marchanderie: Carton et Cie' is the name of the shipper. In some cases the name of the captain of the ship transporting the wine is also added to the label, some such name as Graves or Médoc, and one need not take alarm at this, but one should be instantly suspicious of any marks, names, numbers, or symbols other than those I have gone into here. Bottles which bear such legends as 'George H., Kansas City, '24' or 'C. M. & Bessie B., '18' or 'Mrs. P. P. Bliss, Ashtabula, O., '84' or 'I Love My Wife But Oh You Kid (1908)' may be put down as having fallen into the hands of American tourists somewhere between the bottling and the shipping. They are doubtlessly refills containing a coloured sugar water, if anything at all.

The vintage year is, of course, always branded into the cork of the bottle and is the only kind of bottle-cork date mark to go by. Dates laid in with mother-of-pearl or anything of the sort are simply impressive and invidious attempts to force high prices from the pockets of gullible Americans. So also are French wine labels bearing the American flag or portraits of Washington or such inscriptions, no matter how beautifully engraved or coloured, as 'Columbia, the Gem of the Ocean' and 'When Lilacs Last in the Dooryard Grew'.

In summing up, it is perhaps advisable to say a few words about the vineyards themselves. Some vineyards, facing north, get the morning sun just under the right side of the leaf; others, facing south, get the sun on the other side. Many vineyards slope and many others do not. Once in a while one straggles into a graveyard or climbs up on a porch. In each case a difference may or may not be found in the quality of the wine. When a town has been built on the place where a vineyard formerly was, the vineyard is what the French call 'out' (a word adopted from our English tennis term). There may be a few vines still producing in gutters and backyards of the town, but the quality of their output will be ignoble. The 'out' taste is easily discernible to both the connoisseur and the layman just as is the faint flavour of saddle polish in certain brands of sparkling Burgundy. In the main, it is safe to go by one's taste. Don't let anybody tell you it is one-tenth as hard to tell the taste of a good wine from the taste of a bad wine or even of a so-so wine as some of the *connaisseurs écrivants* would have us believe.

MEMOIRS OF A BANQUET SPEAKER

The sanity of the average banquet speaker lasts about two and a half months; at the end of that time he begins to mutter to himself, and calls out in his sleep. I am dealing here with the young banquet speaker, the dilettante, who goes into it in quest of glamour. There is, he finds out too late, no glamour at banquets – I mean the large formal banquets of big associations and societies. There is only a kind of dignified confusion that gradually unhinges the mind.

Late in my thirty-fifth year, having tasted every other experience in life (except being rescued by Captain Fried), I decided to be a guest of honour at some glittering annual dinner in a big New York hotel. At first blush, you might think it would be difficult to be asked. It isn't. You don't, of course, have to be a member of an organisation in order to address its annual banquet. In fact the organisation doesn't even have to know who you are, and it almost never does. The names of the speakers are got out of newspapers and phone books, and from the better Christmas cards; sometimes a speaker is suggested to the entertainment committee by a woman named Mrs Grace Voynton. That's all I know about her. She suggested me. I never saw her again. As a matter of fact, I never saw her at all. She phoned me one day and asked if I would address the annual banquet of a certain organisation, the name of which, in the ensuing conversation, which was rather controversial, slipped my mind. I said I wouldn't address the banquet because my dinner pants were too tight. She was pleased to regard this as a pleasantry, and phoned me again the next day, as a woman will. Finally I said I would make a short talk. I was told to be at the Commodore Hotel at seven-thirty on a certain Wednesday evening. It was only when I was in a taxi on my way to the hotel that I realised I didn't know the name, or the nature, of the organisation I was going to talk to – let alone what I was going to talk about. So high is the courage of youth that the young banquet speaker is likely to dismiss this unfortunate ignorance too lightly. He has an idea that Mrs Voynton will be at the hotel, or that the doorman will recognise him. Certainly, he thinks, it is going to be easy enough to find the banquet-room. It *isn't* going to be, though (the italics are mine). During the banqueting season anywhere from three to eleven banquets are being held, simultaneously, at the average hotel on any given night. Not realising this, the young guest of honour is almost sure to think that the first banquet table he spies is the one at which he belongs. There is only about one chance in ten that he is right.

I walked into the first banquet-room that I came to, on the mezzanine floor, after having been met by no one at all except a man who asked me where the ladies' dressing-room was. I told him I didn't know and he walked over and told a lady who was with him that I didn't know. There is no reason in the world why a trivial incident like that should unnerve a banquet speaker; it leaves him, however, with a vague sense of insecurity: he begins to wonder where he is, and what night it is, and whether the whole thing may not possibly be a hoax.

In somewhat of a daze – the first warning of a bad mental state – I found myself seated at a long table on a dais, next to a lady who asked me, as soon as I had drunk a glass of ice water, if I understood the makeup and purposes of the organisation we were about to address. She had also accepted over the phone, and had had a miserable connection. I told her facetiously – as one who whistles in the dark to keep his nerve up – that I was under the impression we were the guests of honour at the National Women's Bulb-Raising Association. This caused the man on her right to pale slightly. He drank a little water and whispered to me that, on the contrary, we were at the annual dinner of the North-Eastern States Meat-Handlers Association. I could see, however, that he was uncertain of himself on that point: he kept twisting his napkin. After the coffee and ice cream he was called upon for the first speech of the evening, and if ever a man touched lightly on the meat-handling situation he did. His nervous condition and incoherent remarks obviously upset the toastmaster who, all we speakers were instantly aware, was not absolutely sure that he was at the right banquet himself.

At this point, since I figured that several speakers were yet to come before I would be called on, I slipped from the table and made a hasty trip to the lobby to look up the sign which tells where the various conventions are being held. Several were listed, and their locations were given merely as Ballroom A, Ballroom B, Second Assembly Hall, Jade Room, etc. It was impossible to identify these rooms in the short time at my disposal and so I simply hurried back to my seat. From the sign, however, I had discovered that there was a possibility I might be in the midst of the National Chassis-Builders Association, the Society for the Advancement of Electric Welding, the American Society of Syrup and Fondant Makers, or the Past Presidents and Active Officers of Ye Olde Record Binding Company.

As I sat in my chair, breathing heavily, I tried to think up a few words of greeting and appreciation which might apply equally to the aims and purposes of all the various organisations. This got me nowhere at all. Nor did I receive any help from the gentleman who was talking at the moment. His expression was the agonised expression of a man who hasn't the slightest idea what it is all about and wishes he were home. He told four stories, in a husky voice, and sat down. The toastmaster now arose and said that we were going to have the pleasure of listening to a man who knew more about the subject nearest our hearts than anyone else in America, a man whose great authority in this field has been recognised by his being selected to write on the subject for the new *Encyclopaedia Britannica* (I quote him more or less accurately – it was a little more involved than that). Instead of naming his man at this juncture, the toastmaster told a story, and then reverted to the world's greatest authority on the subject nearest our hearts, repeating what he had already said, and finally, with a sweep of his hand, pronouncing the speaker's name – 'Mr Septimus R. Groves'. As the toastmaster sat down, I lapsed back into my chair and applauded lightly. Nobody got up. All eyes then followed the toastmaster's – and rested finally on me. I knew now that I was at the wrong banquet. Vaguely, as I got to my feet, I wondered where Mr Groves was, and on what subject he was so eminent an authority. I was received with tremendous applause. When it quieted down I began to speak. I sketched briefly the advance of transportation, the passing of riveting, the improvement shown in the handling and distribution of meats, chassis construction, electric welding, and the absolute reliance that one could place nowadays upon the binding of old records. In conclusion I left with my audience the thought that in meat-handling, as in bulb-raising, and binding old records, it is Service and Co-operation that count. The speech was received with thunderous applause and a little stomping.

It was not until I got into a taxi that I realised my mind was already beginning to go. The driver asked me where to. I was surprised to hear myself tell him the Pennsylvania Hotel. There I registered as 'Septimus R. Groves'. 'We already have a Septimus R. Groves registered here,' said the clerk, with polite interest. 'What's his name?' I asked. 'Septimus R. Groves,' he said. 'He's attending the annual banquet of the Fish and Game Wardens.' 'Oh,' I said, 'there must be some mistake; the man you're thinking of is Horace R. Morgner – gypsum blocks and building laths.' The clerk gave me my room key, albeit with a certain reluctance. It was a week before I went home. I don't mutter any longer, but I still cry out in my sleep.

I LIKE DOGS

I am not a dog lover. A dog lover to me means a dog that is in
love with another dog. I am a great admirer of certain dogs, just
as I am an admirer of certain men, and I dislike certain dogs as
much as I dislike certain men. Mr Stanley Walker in his attack
on dogs brought out the very sound contention that too much
sentimental gush has been said and written about man's love
for the dog and the dog's love for man. (This gush, I should say,
amounts to about one ten-thousandth of the gush that has
been printed and recited about man's love for woman, and vice
versa, since Shelley wrote 'O, lift me from the grass! I die, I
faint, I fail! Let thy love in kisses rain on my lips and eyelids
pale.') It is significant that none of the gush about dogs has
been said or written by dogs. I once showed a copy of Senator
Vest's oration to one of my dogs and he sniffed at it and walked
away. No dog has ever gone around quoting any part of it. We
see, then, that this first indictment of dogs – that they have
called forth so much sentimental woofumpoofum – is purely
and simply an indictment of men. I think we will find this to be
true of most of Mr Walker's indictments against the canine
world: he takes a swing at dogs and socks men and women in
the eye.

Mr Walker began his onslaught with a one-sided and prejudiced account of how a *little* red chow *on a leash* (the italics are
mine) pulled a knife on Mr Gene Fowler, a large red man who
has never been on a leash in his life. Neither the dog nor the
woman who was leading the dog are quoted; we don't get their
side of the brawl at all. The knife was not even examined for
paw prints. Nobody proved anything. There isn't a judge in the
world who wouldn't have thrown the case out of court probably with a sharp reprimand for Mr Fowler. So far, then, Mr
Walker hasn't got a leg to stand on.

The next crack that Mr Walker makes is to the effect that the
dog is 'cousin to the wolf'. (He doesn't even say what wolf.)
Now, the dog is no more cousin to the wolf than I am niece to
the horse. I am aware that until very recently, until this year, in

fact, the preponderance of authority has held that the dog is cousin to the wolf. But it happens that remarkable and convincing disproof of this old wives' theory has just been adduced by two able and unimpeachable specialists in the field. Charles Quintus Harbison in his *Myths and Legends of the Dog* (Curtis, Webb – $5.00) and D. J. Seiffert in his *The Canidae, a History of Digitigrade Carnivora* (Green & Barton – $3.50). This disposes of this old superstition in a manner that brooks no contradictions. So much for that.

'The history of the dog', Mr Walker asserts, 'is one of greed. double-crossing, and unspeakable lechery.' Mr Walker, who writes with a stub pen, frequently mislays his spectacles, and is inclined to get mixed up now and then, undoubtedly meant to write, 'The history of man is one of greed, double-crossing, and unspeakable lechery.' If you stopped ten human beings in the street and said to them, 'The history of what animal is one of greed, double-crossing, and unspeakable lechery?' seven would say 'man', two would walk on hastily without saying anything, and the other would call the police. If you put this same query to ten dogs, none of them would say anything (they are much too fair-minded to go around making a lot of loose charges against men) and none of them would phone the police. (I am reminded to say here, speaking of the police, that no dog has ever held a lantern while a burglar opened a safe belonging to the dog's master. A dog's paw is so formed that he cannot hold a lantern. If your burglar is smart *he* holds the lantern while the dog opens the safe.)

It is true that now and then a dog will double-cross his master. I have been double-crossed by dogs sixteen or eighteen times: eighteen, I believe. But I find in going back over these instances that in every case the fault really lay with me. Take the time that a Scottish terrier of mine named Jeannie let me down; it is a classic but, I believe, typical example. I was living some eight or nine years ago in a house at Sneden's Landing, on the Hudson. Jeannie and her seven pups lived in a pen in the dining-room. It would take too long to explain why. The only other person in the house besides me was an Italian cook named Josephine. I used to come out to the house from New York every night by train, arriving just in time for dinner. One evening, worrying about some impending disaster, or dreaming about some old one, I was carried past my station – all the way to Haverstraw, where I had to wait two hours for a train to take me back. I telephoned Josephine from Haverstraw and told her I would not be able to get there until ten o'clock. She was pretty much put out, but she said she would keep dinner for me. An hour before the train arrived to take me back I got so hungry that I had to eat; I ate several sandwiches and drank two cups of coffee. Naturally when I got home finally and sat down at the dining-room table I had no stomach at all for the wonderful dinner Josephine had kept for me. I ate the soup but I couldn't touch any of the steak. When Josephine set it down before me I said 'Wonderful!' in feigned delight and as soon as she went back into the kitchen I cut it up and fed it to Jeannie. We got away with it fine. Josephine was pleased to see my plate licked clean. It looked as if everything was going to be all right and then Josephine set in front of me the largest piece of apple cake I or anybody else had ever seen. I knew how Josephine prided herself on her cake, but I couldn't eat any part of it. So when she went out to the kitchen for the coffee I handed Jeannie the apple cake, hurried to the door which opened from the dining-room into the backyard, and put her out, cake and all. Josephine was in high spirits when she saw with what dispatch and evident relish I had disposed of her pastry. It was while I was in the midst of a long and flowery series of compliments on her marvellously light hand and with a cake that there came a scratching at the door. Josephine went over and opened it. In trotted Jeannie still carrying the apple cake.

Now it is my contention (although it wasn't at the time) that I double-crossed Jeannie as much as she double-crossed me. After all, I had filled her with steak (she had already had her dinner) and then asked her to consume an enormous slice of apple cake. She was only about a foot, foot and a half, two feet long, and it was too much for her. I should have known this. But, you will ask, why didn't she bury it, for God's sake? And why, I will ask you right back, should she? Dogs are trained to take and carry whatever you hand them that isn't edible, and they are not supposed to go and hide it somewhere. To Scottish terriers apple cake is not edible. Jeannie had no way of know-

ing how profoundly she was embarrassing me. A French poodle might have sensed the delicacy of the situation that was bound to develop between me and Josephine if an apple cake which I was supposed to have consumed was carried back into the room by a dog, but a Scottie would never have got the idea. Scotties have barely enough brains to get around (in this they are no worse and no better than men, they are just about the same).

As for Mr Walker's numerous examples of dogs who have broken up affairs, near affairs, and marriages between men and women, I find in a careful examination of each of his instances that it was never the fault of the dog. In every case the dog was simply there and served as an innocent means of revealing the clumsiness of the man and the shallowness of the woman. Let us examine two or three of Mr Walker's case histories. (1) A man sits down on a lady's dog and kills it. The lady turns on the man and throws him out of her life. Mr Walker tells the story as if Lucy (I shall call the dog Lucy) had purposely followed the man around trying to trick him into sitting down on her. As a matter of fact the dog was asleep at the time. Now, the obvious point to be made here is that the man was lucky to get rid of that woman. A husband, or a lover, kills about one fifth of the things he sits down on and if he gets a wife, or a mistress, who raises hell about it, he is going to lead a miserable life. This particular dog, at the sacrifice of its life, saved this particular man from an especially nasty fate. I am saddened that Mr Walker worries about the man in this tragic little triangle. I worry about the dog. The woman, and the man, in this case, might have sighed, after Wordsworth, 'Lucy's in her grave and O, the difference to me.' But I am reminded of a very acute parody of this famous poem in which the parodist altered only one word, the last. He wrote, 'Lucy's in her grave and O, the difference to her.' That's the way I look at that.

Case history No. 2: Mr Walker, calling on a lady whom he intended to take to a masquerade ball, got the lady's dog, a French poodle named Lucille, cockeyed on brandy; in his own words, she was 'stiff as a plank'. The lady came out of the next room, took the situation in at a glance, and refused to go to the ball. Walker left, without taking the poodle with him. Now I submit that to get a poodle drunk and then walk out on her in the very shank of the evening, leaving her to the harsh mercies of a distraught and indignant mistress, is no way for a gentleman to act. A poodle who has had two brandies (they were forced on her, by the way) is just as eager to go out and make a night of it as you and I are. What is more, on her tenth brandy she will prove to be a hell of a sight better companion than most men and women any of us know. Another thing: as a man who has raised dozens of French poodles (and was fond of all seventy-two of them) I can say on firsthand authority that poodles do not like brandy; all they like is champagne and they prefer it in a metal bowl. The fact that Lucille drank brandy with a guest simply proves what a fine hostess she was while batting for her mistress who was in the next room. Mr Walker states at the time of this abortive little drinking bout he was dressed as Sir Walter Raleigh. The poodle would have gone with him anyway; poodles are game for anything.

Case history No. 3: 'A man I know', writes Mr Walker, 'was visiting a lady when a police dog bit the cook in the calf. The woman thought it was the man's fault for some reason . . . Nothing came of that romance, either.' A lucky thing, too, since the woman was obviously feebleminded, blaming something that happened in the kitchen on a gentleman who was sitting in her parlour. In setting out to draw a dark picture of dogs, Mr Walker has succeeded in drawing the gloomiest picture of woman known to the literature of our day. The fact that all of them owned dogs is of no more importance or relevance than the fact that they had grandfather's clocks or runs in their stockings. A disturbing little group of ladies, if you ask me.

I do not believe in any such sentimentality as that man's best friend is the dog. Man's best friend is man. A friend is one who cleaves to you in spite of the left side of your nature, the dark and sticky side. The dog never sees that side. To him you are one fine guy, without any faults, and that of course is not true and you can't build a friendship on something that is not true. Among the things that every man treasures about his best friends are their weaknesses, the mistakes they have made, the dilemmas they have got into. These afford any friend a great deal of material with which to regale dinner parties or entertain a group of the fellas at a table in a bar. A dog, not recognising these weaknesses, mistakes, and dilemmas, never tells anyone about them. A great many of the more famous witty remarks made by New Yorkers in the past ten years were made at the expense of some friend. (Example: Mr W. remarked of his great friend Mr R., 'He is a dishonest Abraham Lincoln.') A dog has no wit.

One time, going through a kennel in Connecticut where people boarded their dogs, I came across a big, handsome brown water spaniel. He stuck a friendly paw out through the bars of his cage as I walked past, tagged me on the shoulder, and I stopped. I was distressed to discover that he had a huge and ugly swelling on one side of his head. I was surprised that in spite of it he was bright-eyed and gay. Suddenly I found out why. He spit out the swelling. It was a big-league baseball which he had just been holding in one cheek until someone came along to play with him. He got way back in the far end of the cage – only about eight feet it was – and looked at the ball and then at me. I spent fifteen minutes bouncing it at him. He could catch the swiftest bounces and never missed once. He made Rabbit Maranville look like a clumsy, fumbling clown. He reminded me of a bull terrier I once had who could catch a baseball thrown as high in the air as you could throw it. I mean you and you and you. A tough guy named Herb Schorey, who could throw a ball as high as any man I have ever seen, lost five bucks betting Rex couldn't catch a ball *he* threw into the air. These are two dogs I have admired.

Rex I liked better than any dog I have ever known and in another place a few years ago I did him some faint, far justice. But I didn't say then and I don't say now that he was the finest and truest and noblest animal that ever lived. The real dog man likes a dog the way he likes a person; the brightest gleam sometimes comes from the flaw. Rex was a gourmand; he twitched and yelped when he slept; he hated Pomeranians and would chew them to bits although he was five times their size; he killed cats; he jumped on horses when they fell down but never tackled one that was on its feet; if you ordered him to stay home he'd slip out the alley gate and meet you five blocks away; he could lick anything this side of Hell and did; he could chin himself with one paw and lift fifty pounds with his jaws; he had a weakness for chocolate ice-cream cones; and although he learned to open the refrigerator door he never learned to close it. The average good dog is that way: I mean the list of his faults would be longer than the sum of his virtues. All in all, Rex was like the men you are fond of – except that when you kill the men they die. Someone beat Rex to death one day but he straight-armed the death angel long enough to wobble home. One of his masters wasn't at the house when he got there (Rex was owned by three brothers), so he stayed alive for three hours by some awful, holy effort that I remember after twenty-five years as clearly as lightning because it was not like anything I have ever seen in the world. When the tardy brother finally arrived home, the dog just managed to touch his hand with his tongue before he dropped dead. Nobody ever more surely earned that long sweet darkness.

If the dog has been ruined for Mr Walker by fulsome song and silly story, by ornate oration and exaggerated editorial, and by the gibberings of half a dozen ghastly gals, then it has been ruined for him, as I said at the beginning of all this, by men and women and not by dogs.

I have no doubt that the dog can be just as biased and prejudiced as man. I am sure there are some dogs who can't stand men just as there are men who can't stand dogs. I don't see that this proves anything. 'I'm always glad', Mr Fowler said, according to Mr Walker, 'when dogs hate me. It's mutual. When a dog attacks me I know I must be all right.'

'When Mr Fowler attacks *me*,' said a prominent dog of my acquaintance recently, '*I* know *I'm* all right. Tell him that when you see him, Mac.' I said I would.

MORE ICE ADDED TO U.S. AS THOUSANDS CHEER

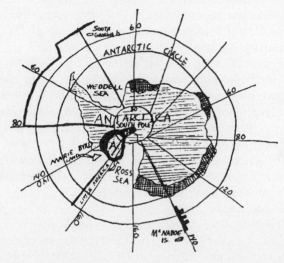

To a great many people, including myself, the newspaper accounts of Admiral Byrd's latest discoveries in the Antarctic a week or so ago made little, if any, sense. I confined my own study of the involved explorations to the *Herald Tribune* article. I reread this article many times and pored over the map that went with it, but for two or three days I couldn't make out what had actually been done and how it had been accomplished. All that I knew for sure was that Byrd had reported to President Roosevelt (who hasn't enough to worry him the way it is) that the recent discoveries had added approximately two hundred thousand square miles of ice to American ice possessions at the South Pole.

I was determined to keep on trying to figure out the article and the map. First I made a map of my own, copying it from the *Herald Tribune* map but making it simpler. My map, for instance, has only thirteen radiating lines, or parallels, as against the *Herald Tribune's* eighteen. This makes the thing a little less confusing, without detracting from the clarity of the chart, because the five lines I left out are of no importance. Nor, indeed, are the thirteen I left in. I would have erased them after I had my map done, but India ink will not erase. I am afraid these parallels are going to handicap my story of the explorations, because they are likely to give the reader the effect of looking at the map through the top of a birdcage.

We now know approximately where we are, without being too technical, but there are one or two other matters regarding the map which I must explain before we get back to Admiral Byrd, if I can find him. The little island at the bottom marked McNaboe Island was marked Macquarie Island on the *Herald Tribune* map and probably is Macquarie Island, but I print my letters so large I couldn't get Macquarie in without running the last two letters into the battleship (lower right). This battleship was not on the newspaper map, and I put it in merely because I had made the mistake of drawing my map from the bottom upward instead of the top down, a system which is bound to cause the heel of the drawing hand to come into contact with, and smudge, lines which have been drawn but have not yet dried. To cover up the smudge I made, I turned it into a battleship. Let it serve as a warning to the Japanese that we do not intend to give up the four hundred thousand square miles of ice we own down there without a struggle.

Now to get back to what actually happened on Byrd's last flight of exploration and discovery. The black area marked B on the map indicates the new ice that has been added to American possessions by the Admiral's recent activities. The dotted area marked A represents the ice that Byrd had discovered previously. It will be noticed at once that the newly discovered ice completely surrounds the previously discovered ice, and a moment's thought will lead one to wonder how this could be. I couldn't figure it out myself for a long time, but finally I decided that that's what comes from exploring in aeroplanes. You can fly right over something without discovering it, discover something further on, and then come back and discover what, if you had been on dog sledges, you would have been bound to discover first.

246

But we *must* get back to what Byrd actually did. He found out, for one thing (and I am going strictly by the newspaper account) that Marie Byrd Land (A and B) is 'a high area with an elevated ice plateau'. I had supposed that everybody knew that already, but it seems no. The region, continues Byrd's wireless, is 'wholly glaciated and overridden by an ice sheet, presumably to a great depth'. This also seems to have come as a surprise to Byrd and his men, but I fancy that President Roosevelt, who is very quick mentally, had suspected it all along. The principal result of Byrd's explorations, however (and I'm *still* sticking to his report to the papers), was the discovery that a long-sought transcontinental strait which was supposed to lie beneath the ice probably does not lie beneath the ice at all, although *maybe* it does. The strait is there, or something like a strait is there (Byrd calls it a passage or depression), but it is, the Admiral says, 'more apparent than real'. That is, it has reality but is also imaginary. In other words, it is something like spots before the eyes, only more icy and expansive. Just because one cannot reach out and touch the spots before one's eyes, it does not prove the spots are not there: and, conversely, simply because one sees them, it does not prove they *are* there.

Byrd established, he says in his report, that 'not far east of this strait (or passage) and to the north and south the plateau descending from Marie Byrd Land curved around and to the south, so that no such passage could exist'. I have been over that sentence a dozen times, and I have finally come to the conclusion that Admiral Byrd was lost. I think he was lost, and I think he was too proud to say so. After all, he had been gone on this flight six hours and forty-four minutes and he had to say *something* when he got back.

Another thing the Admiral discovered (and this seems to be the most important discovery of all) is that 'from the 75th parallel [never mind seeing the map] to the Pole, a stretch of one thousand miles, it is all land, overwhelmed by ice to be sure, but land anyhow'. Of course, this overwhelm of ice is several thousand feet thick and always will be, but President Roosevelt will be glad to know that underneath it all there is land. To be sure, we cannot get at the land, but it belongs to us and always will belong to us, unless, of course, there should some day come a huge ice slide which would cause all the ice to move away from the South Pole, like a tremendous glacier, leaving the land bare. In that case it is doubtful whether the United States could establish its claim to the land, because, after all, Byrd stuck the American flag in the ice. In some cases he didn't come within a mile of the land underneath. I should think, therefore, that in the event the ice did move off, Byrd or somebody else (and I have an idea it would be Byrd) might have to go back and reclaim all the land for America by sticking flags in it. Furthermore, if the ice we now own should, in moving off, end up on the shores of Australia, say, and finally completely cover that continent, I doubt very much that Great Britain would even recognise our claim to the ice, let alone our claim to the land underneath it (Australia).

To return to the map for a moment (and if anybody has been wondering, I haven't the slightest idea what the heavy black zigzag line means), you will notice that compared to the great expanse of shaded area marked Antarctica, Byrd's ice accumulations so far are absolutely trivial. Everything shown on this map is ice, or ice-and-land, or ice-on-land, except the white areas, which are water (note Ross Sea and Weddell Sea – named for the mysterious and inaccessible old Weddell house). My estimate may be wrong, because there was no scale of miles on the map I copied, but I should judge that if the whole shaded area (Antarctica, or Marie Byrd Land) is finally discovered and claimed for America, we will possess, in all, about 28,700,000 square miles of ice. It is not a thing to contemplate blandly. It is high time that America woke up and realised that every year hundreds of thousands of square miles of ice are being added to her possessions, and that our pride in this accumulation is, after all, based on no sounder reason than that somewhere underneath all this ice there lies, or may lie, some land. Are we landowners or ice dealers? Are we men or penguins? Let us face these questions soberly.

THE STORY OF THE BICYCLE

Although the bicycle has not multiplied anywhere near as rapidly as the rabbit, it must be borne in mind that in the beginning there was only one bicycle whereas there were two rabbits. It is perhaps unfortunate that both the vehicle and the animal are just about the same today as they were to begin with. They have not reached a very high point of development; they are not, as a matter of fact, really Getting Anywhere. This, to be sure, is also true of the bugle, the beagle, the button, and practically everything else. Indeed, one of the few things I can think of at the moment which have really made appreciable progress is Woman. (See Figs 1 and 2).

Fig. 1 *Early Woman*

However, we are getting off the subject, for this lecture is to be concerned solely with the origin and progress, such as it has been, of the wheel. I am sorry, but that is what it is to be concerned with. Next month, if you are good little boys and girls, I shall tell you something more about Woman.

Fig. 2 *Modern Woman*

The first wheel constructed by the hand of man was square. This played hell with the early charioteers, who were jiggled and jerked and bumped about during races and battles like so many jumping jacks in a windstorm. Acutely uncomfortable as it was, this type of wheel was used for several centuries, until, in fact, the year 247 B.C., when a Greek named Thycides, by cutting off each point of the square wheel, brought into existence the octagonal wheel. This was something of an improvement, but not much, for as one famous charioteer of the period observed, 'Maybe she don't jolt you as high as she once did, but she jolts you twice as often.' The truth of this observation becomes immediately apparent when you study Figs 4 and 5. (Fig. 3 has been lost.) When Thycides had fitted the new octagonal wheels to his chariot, he called to his wife to come out and see

Fig. 4

Fig. 5

what the genius of Man had brought to pass. She went out and looked. 'Now we're getting somewheres!' cried Thycides, as he jolted around the backyard. 'Are we?' said his wife, coldly, and she went back to cleaning the silver. Undaunted, Thycides went round and round and as the octagonal wheels turned and turned their edges gradually wore smooth and the round wheel as we know it today came into existence (Fig. 6). (Fig. 6 has also disappeared.)

In the centuries that followed, mankind adjusted round wheels to the cart, the wagon, the dray, the buckboard, the phaeton, the surrey, the stagecoach, and the horsecar. It did not, however, occur to the human being until 1871 that a thing with only two wheels, one in front of the other, could be made to stay upright while you were on it. The idea had never crossed Archimedes' mind, and Galileo was always too busy with something else. It finally remained for Charles Bekkel, the inventor of the two-wheeled bicycle, to demonstrate the fact that if you rode 'er fast enough and didn't jiggle 'er too much, she would stay upright. Like Thycides before him, he shouted to his wife to come and witness what he, with the help of the Almighty, had figured out. She went out into the dooryard. 'I can ride on two wheels, Maude!' cried Bekkel. 'Lookit, I can ride on two wheels!' His wife viewed the noisy proceedings briefly. 'Remember you got your Sunday pants on,' she said, and went back to her Mason jars.

In 1884 there were only seventeen bicycles in Washington, D.C. When this is compared to the figures for 1894, which I have unfortunately mislaid, it will be seen, or would be if we had the figures, that the increase had been remarkable. The increase continued to be remarkable in the United States until 1904, when suddenly there was a terrific drop. America had discovered sex. The whole country immediately lost interest in the bicycle and began to play pillow, Post Office, footy-footy, and house. Today there are not more than sixty-five hundred bicycles in New York State, or in the country at large. I can't remember which. And what was the rabbit doing all this time? Let us take a peep and see. In the past seventy years the total number of bicycles in the world has lagged far behind the total number of rabbits. There is considerable room for doubt as to whether, short of a rabbit purge, or a bicycle boom, or both, the two figures will ever reach a parity. In Australia alone there are more than 75,569,132 rabbits. Some of you may find it interesting to compare this figure with the numbers one frequently sees on the sides of New York Central freight cars.

The highest number that I personally have ever encountered on a freight car was 56798720483342. This is exactly 15,347 times as large as the total number of bicycles that have been manufactured in the entire world since the installation of the first official U.S. government Weather Bureau (March 3, 1839). That bureau, we might notice in passing, was set up by one John R. Strobe, in Fond du Lac (Bottom of the Lake), Wis. (Wisconsin). Strobe, possibly as a result of his long years of solitude in his hut at the furthest point of Cape Gleason, took to playing nine men's morris with a bottle full of fireflies, and had to be replaced in 1857.

A question which is frequently asked of me takes this form: 'Is the bicycle here to stay?' It is difficult to say. We all know, of course, that in the past thirty years the bicycle has taken a pretty bad tossing around from the automobile and from certain low-flying aeroplanes. There is probably no more upsetting experience in the world than to be 'clipped' by the wing of an aeroplane as you cycle idly along some lovely old country road whose hedges are sweet with eglantine. Nobody can safely predict anything – although everybody I know spends most of his time predicting everything – but I should like to hazard the guess that if this clipping continues at its present rate everybody with any brains at all will give up the bicycle and take to the woods on foot.

This inevitably brings us to the question of how many people there are with any brains at all. My own investigations have resulted in some rather depressing findings. They show, among other things, that seventeen percent of the male population of the world cool their porridge with their hats, and that eighty-seven percent of all women throw a baseball with their right foot advanced. Moreover, seven persons out of every ten believe that the common toad causes warts and this in spite of the fact that it has a precious jewel in its head! Many of my findings are too disconcerting to go into.

If you will all quit rustling your programmes and sit still for a moment, I shall tell you, in closing, the ill-fated story of Charles R. Butterost. Butterost, who for forty-five years had ridden bicycles, kiddy-kars, taxi-cabs, and aeroplanes, without feeling that any of them had really got him anywhere, one afternoon climbed into a baby carriage at the top of a hill, pulled the pink coverlet up to his chin, started her down the hill at a breakneck pace, and shot himself through the head as he went.

I am not recommending this as a way out, I am just telling you.

I BREAK EVERYTHING I TOUCH

I am interested in forming a little club of miserable men. No man can belong to it who can fix anything or make anything go. No man can belong to it who is handy around the house – or the garage, or anywhere else.

I was born with an aversion to tools. When I was in the eighth grade I had to go to manual-training class every Thursday and I was still planing away at a breadboard when the other boys were putting the finishing touches on kitchen cabinets, davenports, and pianos. The breadboard was as far as I ever got and when I finally had it done the instructor, a temperamental and highly strung man named Buckley, who really loved carpentry and cabinet-making, picked it up and looked at it and said, 'Thurber, I weep for you.' I wept for me, too. I was covered with cuts and bruises from gouges, planes, bits-and-braces, saws, and hatchets. None of the other boys had a mark on them.

The only thing I can really do is change the ribbon on a typewriter, but it took me twenty-two years to learn that and every now and then I have to call in a friend or neighbour to help unravel me. When I was younger, I once changed a fuse in the fuse box, but I am too old and too smart to try that again. They tell me that electricity has been harnessed, and I say yes and so was King Kong. I don't even like to monkey with the thermostat that regulates the oil furnace. Every time I put the thing down to 55° before going up to bed, I expect to be blown out through the roof.

I come by my ineptitude with contraptions of any kind quite naturally. My grandmother on my mother's side was afraid of doorbells; she always took the receiver off the telephone hook during a thunderstorm: she believed that if you unscrewed an electric light bulb, electricity would drip invisibly all over the house and if you then struck a match, you would be blown to Hell. My mother was confident that the Victrola we bought in 1913 would explode if you wound it too tight, and she was forever warning me not to drive the family Reo without gasoline, because she had heard it was bad for it if you did.

About the only thing I really know about an automobile is that you can't run it without gasoline. The Lord knows that enough of my men friends have explained the principles of the gas engine to me, but I am always just where I was when they started – and so is the gas engine. For all I know, the distributor regulates the pressure on the manifold. I can run a car and I can stop one; I can also turn right and left and back up; but I don't know exactly what is happening. The thing has never become any more clear to me than the third law of thermodynamics – or the first one, as far as that goes.

I have, of course, been in any number of embarrassing situations with automobiles, from my grandfather's old Lozier to my 1935 Ford. In England (I drove fifteen thousand miles in Europe and lived to tell it) my battery went dead near one of the cathedral towns, and I phoned a garage. A young mechanic in a truck appeared after a while and said he would pull me and I could get my engine started that way. I had been pulled and pushed in the old Reo days and I knew that you could start the engine that way. I knew that you pushed the clutch in (or is it out?) and then let it out (or in) suddenly. So the garage man attached a rope to the back of his truck and to the front of my car and away we went – over the hills and through the dales of England.

Every quarter mile or so he would stop and come back to me to see what was the matter. He lifted the hood, he got under the car, but there was nothing doing.

At the end of five or six miles he got out and said, 'What gear you got her in?' He had me there. I didn't have her in any gear. I had her in neutral. He just stared at me, not in anger or resentment, not with an injured look, but as Cortez must have stared when he stumbled on the Pacific. I know now that you can't make her turn over if you've got her in neutral, but I don't know why. You can make her turn over with the starter when you've got her in neutral. The hell with it.

My worst embarrassment came one day in Connecticut when my engine began to heat up until the red fluid in the gauge was almost up to the top. I stopped at a garage and pointed this out to a mechanic. I got out of the car and stood looking in at the dashboard, thus seeing it from an unfamiliar angle.

Suddenly I saw what I thought was the matter. A needle on one of the dials pointed to 152. 'For God's sake!' I said to the mechanic, 'that shouldn't be registering so high, should it?' (I always swear around mechanics to make them think I have an easy, profane knowledge of motors.) The garageman gave me a long, puzzled look – the old Cortez look. 'That's your radio dial, brother,' he said.

Sure it was. I just hadn't recognised it. Half the time I look at the oil-pressure gauge instead of the speedometer and I think I am doing only seventeen miles an hour.

One of the presents I got for Christmas was a handsome newfangled soda syphon complete with a set of directions. I put the thing away until just the other day, and then I got the directions out and looked at them, the way ladies look at the snakes in a zoo.

The first three directions were simple enough but the fourth began to make me suspicious. It reads like this: 'Place a Super-Charger in the charge holder with small end pointing out (see Figure C). Then screw back cap of charge holder. Do not use force.' They don't know that the first thing I use is force – I use it on linked-nail puzzles and olive bottles and everything else. An engineer or a mechanic or my brother-in-law or the next-door neighbour would go about a thing like this simply and gently, but what I do is get panic-stricken, the way you would if somebody grabbed you in a dark room, and the first thing you know I have the contraption on the floor with my knee on its chest. Pretty soon something makes a sharp snapping noise and the device has to be taken to the attic to join all the other contrivances whose bones I have broken in a series of unequal struggles. Psychologists would explain this by saying that I don't really want the things around so I break them while pretending to be trying to make them work. Psychologists are often right.

But to get back to the syphon. Rule Six says: 'To puncture Super-Charger and to charge the syphon push down charging button (marked A in Figure D) with heel of hand (see Figure E); or give button a tap with palm of hand. Some people find it easier to push charging button against edge of kitchen sink or table.' I haven't got up enough courage yet to experiment with this syphon, for while I am sure it would work fine for nine men out of ten, I have a feeling it would fight to a draw with me. Next year the makers might even have to add a line or two to Rule Six: 'Mr Thurber of Woodbury, Connecticut, finds it easier to grasp the syphon with both hands and whang it against the kitchen stove. See Group F: the cut and bleeding figure is Thurber.'

When I was twelve years old, an uncle gave me a little box Brownie, the simplest camera in the world. A folder of directions came with it, and I warily approached the section where it explained how to put in a film. 'First,' it said, 'spring out the spool pins.' I knew right there the thing had me. I knew that far from being able to spring out the spool pins, I wouldn't be able to find them. I gave the camera to the first little boy I met on the street, a youngster of eight, who I was sure could spring out the spool pins with his eyes blindfolded and mittens on his hands.

This is not the world for me, this highly mechanised world. I can only hope that in Heaven there is nothing more complicated than a harp and that they will have winged mechanics to fix mine when I get down and break its back.